The EM Discoveries

The EM Discoveries

an Account
of
the Three Technological Wonders
That Opened the EM Age

by
Robert Gibbons

EXPOSITION PRESS   **HICKSVILLE, NEW YORK**

Contents

Acknowledgements

The author acknowledges the following relevant and inspirational comments from history—by men of far better letters:

Fontenelle, A.D. 1797 (his remark about his new book on Infinite Geometry):
> Here is a book that only eight men in France are capable of understanding, and the author is not one of that number.

Oliver Wendell Holmes, A.D. 1920:
> As I grow older I grow calm. If I feel what are perhaps an old man's apprehensions, I do not lose my hopes. I do not pin my dreams for the future to my country or even to my race. I think it probable that civilization somehow will last as long as I care to look ahead. I think it is not improbable that man, like the grub that prepares a chamber for the winged thing it has never seen but is to be—that man may have cosmic destinies that he does not understand. And so beyond the vision of battling races and an impoverished earth I catch a dreaming glimpse of peace.

Charles A. Lindbergh, A.D. 1970 (National Science Policy Hearings):
> Our civilization can be destroyed if man does not learn to control the fantastic forces of the various technologies our scientific knowledge has released.

Walter Lippmann, A.D. 1971:

> What kind of civilization will come out of the technological revolution I don't pretend to forsee. I think it would be presumptuous and rather foolish to try to forsee it.

William Josephs, A.D. 1985 (P.M.I. Propulsion Conference, Plum Brook, Ohio):

> It is for each man, according to his innermost substance, either to acknowledge or to turn away from his convictions of human purpose and Providential Plan.

Prologue:
The Next
Major Scientific Breakthrough

"The Next Major Scientific Breakthrough" has been both a speculative thesis and a propelling inspiration for mankind in all of time. Since the first Scientific Discovery—shall we say, that of the Wheel, by Stone Age man perhaps a full million years ago—every cultural progress of our human race has drawn breath and nourishment from the succession of Major Scientific Breakthroughs down through the Ages. And, though we humans realize that we are Earth's specially favored creatures, we cannot cease to consider in awe our role and our destiny in the Universe; for each and every one of these Scientific Breakthroughs has been a timely and providential grant to the human race—a new thread of knowledge that Nature has yielded and revealed of itself.

Discovery, as apart from technological invention, implies a new expansive insight into the basic, closely guarded secrets of Nature. There is no doubt that within each Discovery there is a certain amount of invention, and a few inventions, themselves, approach discovery classification. But an added factor of distinction between the two classifications is the relevancy of the new knowledge to the times. True definition, then, in this temporal sense, requires an inspection of the before and after. Prior to the event—the Discovery or invention—what was the state of man's ignorance or deprivation? And following the event, what degree of change or revolution did it bring to his mode of life—to his culture? What opportunities for human emergence toward man's full and complete purpose came from this new increment of knowledge?

Was Stone Age man's discovery of the Wheel a great breakthrough—or was it just another invention? Here, the relevancy of the event to that early time in history gives us the answer. The simple Wheel, as one of the caveman's stone tools, probably was the first noteworthy technological invention. Yet, in a consideration of the prior state of primitive man's ignorance, and of the subsequent millions of applications in Stone, Bronze, Iron, and Steel, and of the continuing innovative assignments of the mechanical principle of the Wheel, we can assuredly say that this "invention" was relevantly and truly a Discovery. There are a few other simple tools of mechanical leverage, such as the Wheel, that can claim such recognition. Most of these inventions trace their technical principles back to prior Discoveries or simply to "common sense" applied to a specific technological need.

The big Discoveries in history—the Scientific Breakthroughs —have marked their importance to man's cultural evolution by hanging their names onto the Ages of Man. Man's time on Earth began with the Stone Age, by far the longest—at least a million years in time and human struggle. And this dawning of human culture carries the name of the stone Wheels and other stone tools that served our earliest ancestors. After the endless span of this formative Age, there finally began in 5000 B.C. the parade of the relatively short-term Ages of "modern" time. Copper opened the Age of Metals, followed by Bronze, Iron, and Steel. Then, in turn, came the Steam or Engine Age, and the Nuclear Age of Man. And of course, the past 1,000 years mark our present point in time, the EM Age, which began with the fabulous EM Discoveries of A.D. 1985. From the Stone Age's Wheel to the 20th century's awesome Nuclear reactor, every Scientific Breakthrough had served its Age and its discoverers well; but there were facets of every Discovery that found application as often in the destruction of man as in his aid. And no man in history was more exposed to make this critical observation than 20th-century man, in the years just before the beginning of our wondrous EM Age. The 20th-century man lived in a world beset on every quarter with serious, survival-type problems, in a world gravely divided in its social, economic, and nationalistic outlooks. We may well imagine that a concerned 20th-century observer, one day, might have paused in his tracks to contemplate and to assess the Ages of history, in order to understand his own precarious time. On such a reflective occasion he could have asked: Has there been, in all of man's history, one most beneficent, most important Scientific Breakthrough?

Now, a search for the champion of Scientific Breakthroughs may seem to be purely an interesting academic question—to satisfy 20th-century man's compulsion for record-keeping. But, in fact, it is a reasonable question of history, and one that would have received a direct reply from the historians of that time; for they were in complete accord on the subject. Their response would be that the greatest scientific event of all time did happen— not suddenly, but gradually—between 5000 B.C. and 3000 B.C. with man's cultural transition from the Stone Age into the Age of Metals.

The Discovery of Metals, and the subsequent applications of metal technologies to the arts and sciences, was indeed revolutionary and has affected all aspects of man's livelihood and culture even into our present time. That this new knowledge—the Science of Metals—stimulated the pace of man's progress, and that great societies and nations have prospered in the later Iron and Steel Ages, cannot be disregarded. These are the facts of history. Yet, a closer look at the record—confirming our 20th-century observer's suspicions—indicates that all was not in complete harmony during the 7,000 years from the Copper-Bronze through the Steel Ages. To the searching, truth-seeking eye it appears that these seven millennia invoked and supported an undercurrent of disharmony among men. There is evidence of an air of confusion in which the competing motivations of men, and also of nations, took their turns at the "top of the hill." It seems, from the record, that the Age of Metals fostered a separation and divergence of the valued philosophies, rather than their unification. Wars on regular cycle, fears of wars, distrust between peoples and nations, material acquisition as the ultimate goal—on both the personal and national levels: all of these discreditable "achievements" are evident during the 7,000-year span of the Age of Metals. Continuing technological advances in the Steam and Nuclear Ages did nothing to relieve the confusion, and almost as if in a disservice to Science, late 20th-century "successes" in the development and deployment of multiple war-headed ICBMs augmented the self-destructive trend that threatened world society.

Now, as I write in the closing years of the 30th century A.D., we are approaching the millennial anniversary of the EM Age of Man. Perhaps first—1,000 years after the fact, and in a voice presuming to speak for all the human race—we should congratulate ourselves on having made it beyond the 20th-century and into an era that does not know political or social strife. Yet, we note that our EM Age is not different from the other Ages in man's history; at least in the respect that it, too, began with a Major Scientific Breakthrough. But the Discovery of the 100 EM Rayforms in A.D. 1985 heralded an age that really cannot be compared, in the same terms, with any previous segment of man's tenure on the Earth. The EM Discoveries of A.D. 1985 gave us an Age founded upon a harmony in the motivations of nations and individuals alike. And the measure of Humanistic, as well as Scientific, progress in EM time makes all previous history appear to have been tied to the starting post.

The Scientific Breakthrough that spawned the EM Age is the basic subject underlying the story of *The EM Discoveries*—and of the three Technological Wonders that introduced the Age. While such a subject, a Major Scientific Breakthrough, often finds expression as a fictional forward speculation, our story is an accounting, a reflection backward to the EM Discoveries of A.D. 1985. By this approach we are able to write with an advantage of accuracy inherent only to historical retrospect. And while such an advantage and attention to accuracy ensure credibility, they also run the risk of burdening the reader with common, already well-known details of our EM environment. To avoid this failure, we suggest that he may want to play the game of placing himself backward in time, into the reading chair of his 20th-century counterpart. Thus transposed, today's 30th-century man will discover that the everyday elements of EM Technology have become fantasies beyond his wildest speculative projection.

One authorial purpose of *The EM Discoveries* is to recall to the citizens of our EM World Federation the relative levels of the world's culture 1,000 years ago and now. And also, as a collection of operational details correlated to fundamental EM Scientific principles, the essays within *The EM Discoveries* may serve as a kind of manual of the technologies of our time. It should be recognized, of course, that the essays relate only partial descriptions of some of the better known Technological Wonders of the Age. If these limited accounts help to explain even in a small-way "what lies under the hood," or to tell what makes the EM top spin, *The EM Discoveries* will have fulfilled an end.

Additionally, there is—more by implication than by subjective detail—the further intention that each reader may draw, or perhaps "discover," his own provocations from the essayed topics. In this regard, it may happen that a sense of individual and personal appreciation for our good fortune and Providential guidance will compound itself with an increased understanding of the material accomplishments of EM Technology—or perhaps not; for such a sense and attitude arise from a personal and private decision.

And so, the stories of the three founding technological Wonders, in keeping with the expansive characteristic of our Age, are not intended to be limited in their perspectives to the technical and engineering attributes of EM Science. With each passing century we have perceived that man is moving ahead—indeed, is being pulled forward—in all the fields of human purpose. Many men of wisdom in our Councils say that our present Age, like all of the previous increments along man's evolutionary course, is but another phase of training and preparation on our continuing "Transcendental Voyage." If this is so—and there seem to be no sound reasons to believe otherwise—there will continue to be further grants of knowledge—Scientific Breakthroughs—from Nature. They will be timely to our purpose, but unexpected. They will be logical, but surprising in their content. Concerning the exciting and fascinating prospect that *is* the Future, one thing is certain. The "Next Major Scientific Breakthrough" most assuredly will produce changes—yes, revolutions—in our environment, in our livelihoods, and in our lives—far beyond our present limited imaginations.

The EM Discoveries

CHAPTER I

Weather And Climate Control

EM Technology Solves the Weather Problem

BY WAY OF INTRODUCTION, AND DIRECTION— WHAT WOULD OUR ANCESTORS THINK?

If we were able to tune backward in time, 1,000 years into history, to communicate with our 20th-century predecessors—and to tell them face to face that shortly after their time hurricanes, tornadoes, and all types of violent Weather were never again to be permitted on Earth, we undoubtedly would be greeted with an unkindly coldness, or at least the arching of their ancestral eyebrows in disbelief. But certainly, even though our pre-EM Age ancestors might question the veracity of our statements, their curiosity and interest would be aroused; for mankind, up to their time, had always been at the mercy of the variance and violence of Weather, and had longed to understand this most powerful and wildest facet of Nature.

Let's assume for narrative sake that somehow—shall we say through a magic of mental electronics—we have made this ethereal contact backward into the 1970s; and that we have achieved a confrontation with our beloved, though scientifically inept, forebears. Let's tell them that not only have their progeny solved the Earth's Weather Problem, but that EM Age people have lived for nearly 10 centuries under a worldwide system of man-made Electromagnetic "umbrellas" that reach upward 10 miles into the atmosphere to control the temperature and moisture of the air, the force of the winds, and the amounts of Solar-input and Terrestrial-reradiated energies. And we could tell them that in our EM technological sophistication, we even dare to schedule the times and depths of our rainshowers. But rainshowers à la carte might be too much for their imaginations—beyond the comprehension of these old friends, our beloved ancestors. They logically could turn away from us and scoff at what they surely would deem to be the pipe dreams of their irresponsible descendants.

Yet, this rare retro-communication that we now hold with them should not be wasted. It may be decades before we again can achieve such a clear contact. So we must chance their understanding and tolerance. Let's go ahead and tell them all of the news about the EM Weather Control System and how it has been expanded during the past 1,000 years to include the Climate Improvement and Land Reclamation Program. Who knows but that our forefathers of the 20th century might even be proud of the stewardship of their progeny, when we show them how more than 30 million square miles of the finest agricultural land—an area greater than 50% of the total Earth land surface—have been added to the service of mankind, salvaged from the Earth's once arid wastelands by EM Technology working in the Climate Improvement and Land Reclamation Program.

We should tell them—as we routinely do in the elementary school curricula of all EM Age children—how the Weather Control System pumps millions of tons of "adsorbed water vapor" from the oceans to distant inland stations via Rayform atmospheric pipelines. We should describe how Rayform #17 and #27 umbrellas induce synthetic, gentle weather fronts, and how thousands of local 10-mile x 10-mile Weather Control sites are used to scrub away those stagnant smogs that had always been a plague over the world's large cities. And, at least, we ought to give them a brief account of our wonderful globe-circling OMNI System of Weather Control—how it has been employed by EM technologists to modify the extremes of the frigid and of torrid climates, and of the part the OMNI System plays in the redistribution of reconstituted and "Elementally Separated" materials to the Land Reclamation areas of the Earth.

But, on second thought, perhaps we are going too fast, in our eagerness to broadcast the successes of the EM Age. It might be less disappointing—safer and saner at any rate—to simply and singularly *wish* that we could tell our 20th-century predecessors about Weather Control and about the other wonders of the OMNI System. The actual telling, even if our 1,000-year backward communication were possible, would probably be in vain. Truthfully, we could not hope for much. The old folks, even in their Valhalla, would never believe such a fantasy. And that, alas, is what they would assess our story to be.

We should not be overly disappointed by our presumed failure to gain understanding—or is it recognition that we seek from them?—because this is the way it is between generations, and the aggravation after a millennium of separation will be in proportion. Elders have always been skeptical of the dreams of youth; perhaps because in their love for them, most parents do not want to see their children engage in the precarious pursuits of the Scientific future—pursuits that sometimes approach the edge of reason.

It is better, after all—and in line with our second thoughts— that we stay in the world of reality in our communications. Therefore, this story of Weather and Climate Control should and will be directed to our contemporaries. Particularly, it will be pointed to those EM Age citizens who are searching for an understanding of the basic scientific principles that give foundation to EM Weather Control Technology. People of our time are the everyday recipients of the wonders and comforts of Weather Control. And since seeing is believing, our subject would not in the least be suspect to them, as it would be to the ancients of the 20th century. We can, however, easily forgive our sturdy forefathers for their disbelief—which we arbitrarily ascribe to them. In their era they did not yet have occasion to witness the technological miracles that started to come to mankind just after their time— at the end of the 20th century.

On our course, we will keep in mind the state of Natural privation that was extant prior to A.D. 2000. The struggles of our ancestors with the fury of Weather and with the harshness of Climates are vivid parts of their history that serve to stabilize our own appreciation of the EM Wonders we routinely enjoy. In an indirect way, then, as we recognize our debt to those 20th-century ancestors, we truly are in contact. And perhaps, when in time we

all join their ranks, we may be surprised to discover, contrary
to our hasty judgment, that they have, in their eternity, known all
this while the facts that we are about to relate—the story of
Weather and Climate Control in the EM Age.

HOW THE WEATHER CONTROL IDEA STARTED
THE EM DISCOVERIES OF A.D. 1985

From recorded history we learn that progress in the physical
sciences, as measured by man's technological achievements upon
Earth, was virtually at a snail's pace until the 19th and 20th centuries. During these two centuries there finally was a kind of
awakening among scientific thinkers, an awakening that did produce a few measureable advances in the technologies of electricity,
metallurgy, aviation, electronic communication, and nuclear adaptation. In fairness, it can be said that the pace of progress in the
20th century gradually quickened, at least to that of the tortoise.
While it may seem that modern EM Age reviewers berate 20th
century and earlier progress, such a minimal assessment of those
early achievements is fair and reasonable, in comparison. For,
with the coming of the EM Age, heralded by William Josephs'
announcement of the 100 "Forms of Electricity"— the 100 EM
Rayforms—in A.D. 1985, there began an advancement in Science
and Technology that dwarfs any measure of progress in all of
previous time.

The EM Discoveries brought scientific man out of his confinement into a world as large and as eventful as he dared to
imagine. The 100 keys that opened this new world of scientific
opportunity were Josephs' EM Rayforms. These fabulous new
servants and friends of man had the power and the capability of
100 genies, to bring about a series of new technologies on Earth
as immense in their physical enormity as they were in the magni-
ficence of their service to mankind.

In keeping with the bold spirit and the gigantic prospects of
their Discovery, it was natural for the EM pioneers to focus their
attention onto an equally gigantic challenge—the Control of Weather. Almost audible in their influence on the pioneers' decision were

two exciting new Rayforms, which were among the first on the scene to reveal their long held natural secrets. These two were the well-known Rayform #17, the "Water Carrier"; and Rayform #27, the Solar Radiation Adsorber. Rayforms #17 and #27, it can be imagined, must have begged for a daring application to prove their worth and to give full exposition to their potentialities. Weather Control was the obvious, almost automatic choice to test these two new EM "genies." And a fortunate and rewarding choice it certainly was; for, from the engineering and operational experience related to the first Weather Control apparatus have come thousands of inventions and sub-technologies. Our worldwide coordination, the EM OMNI System, evolved from the first Weather Control installations. Even today, the OMNI System follows the basic 10-mile x 10-mile square W.C. (Weather Control) pattern suggested by Josephs' team in A.D. 1985. Present-day methods of energy distribution, of the logistics of both raw and in-cycle materials, and of the traffic coordination of our P.M.I. (Projected Magnetic Image) Propulsion vehicles all have their foundations in the system of EM technology known as Weather and Climate Control.

William Josephs and his team foresaw that the extremes of Weather could be modified and dampened by building a huge EM Rayform "canopy" over selected sections of the land. Their vision toward the future proposed that control of Weather's extremes would be much like raising an umbrella overhead when the bright sunshine was putting excessive, threatening energy into an already unstable air mass whose moisture and enthalpic contents presaged a weather violence. And under an opposite set of meteorological determinants, when the air mass had become dry and cloudless allowing the Sun relentlessly to scorch the underlying Earth, they foresaw that the umbrella could be used to shade upper air levels while EM Rayform water-carriers were employed to condition lower levels with an appeasing water injection.

On the grand scale these farsighted EM pioneers visualized Weather and Climate Control even as we know it today—where many 10, 100, and 1,000-mile square control zones would be interlocked and coordinated, operating day and night under the guidance of Weather System Energy-Balance Computers. Vertically beamed sensors, probing upward from every 10-mile station, would continuously gather data defining local air mass gradients. This information would feed the input end of Comparator-Computers in Weather Central working on the Weather Energy-Balance Equation. The thousands of 10-mile x 10-mile local unit stations would, in turn, respond to the Computer solution by regulating Solar input energy, Earthly (terrestrial) heat radiation, and by adjusting their local air mass moisture contents. All of these startling capabilities had become feasible with man's new knowledge of EM Science and with his ability to control the prodigious Rayforms. Generations of work in design and development lay ahead, but the Weather Control idea had taken root simultaneously and spontaneously with the EM Discoveries.

Needless to say, the expansive possibilities offered by the new EM Science and the ambitious range of its pioneering projects were enough to stagger the imaginations of even the most broadminded citizens back in A.D. 1985. Therefore, while Weather Control and other proposed EM technologies foretold benefits beyond measure for the inhabitants of the World, it was important to present such revolutionary concepts to the people of that day in a manner that would earn their confidence and acceptance. During the 15 years following the historic EM Discoveries, Josephs and his team dedicated their lives to this end. Their revelation and presentation to the nations of the World, in A.D. 2000 of the first 100-square mile prototype area of Controlled Weather and Modified Climate was a wonder to behold. This culmination of their work, the Wamsutter, Wyoming, 10-mile x 10-mile Controlled Weather Area, was and still is today a great monument to EM Science. Additionally, and of crucial political importance, Wamsutter played a distinguished role in convincing the distraught World nations of that era to abandon their mutual distrusts and international rivalries, and to join in a worldwide cooperative effort for peace—by their united participation and sharing in the new EM Technologies. The enthusiastic and grateful worldwide acceptance of all three EM prototype projects (Weather Control,

Elemental Separation, and P.M.I. Propulsion) in A.D. 2000 marked the beginning in history of the EM Age of Man.

TAMPERING WITH NATURE?
——or FILING OUR CONSTRUCTION PERMIT

Before we dig into the bricks and mortar and other operational details of Weather and Climate Control Technology, we ought to take a look at two important background subjects: the Natural or normal atmosphere of the Earth before EM Age technology modified it; and our human attitudes about "tampering" with it. Let us deal with the "conscience" problem first.

Some citizen-technicians, even in our era of fifth-level mental perception, in fits of soul-searching, may ponder, "What a gigantic case of vanity that we should be so bold to alter the Weather and Climates, to disrupt the Natural programming of the elements— and in so doing, possibly to incite the Creator to a vengeance against man for his unholy tampering within the very realm of Providence." Most of us today, however, would consider such a self-indicting attitude as excessively inhibited and narrow-minded in the enlightened view of man's purpose under God. For—we should ask ourselves—is not our resignation and submission to inclement, destructive Weather, and to a tolerance of those uninhabitable desert-like and frigid environments of Earth, any different than our submission to the other burdens of life imposed on us by our own ignorance? Have we forgotten those several dark and stagnant periods in history when man's mental simplicity made him the slave of tyrants—and the spiritless victim of Natural privations, the least of which has been Weather and Climate?

But man's finest attribute, on his transcendental voyage, may well be his irrepressible, nondeniable search for knowledge and Science—for a better way to do his work on Earth, to fulfill his destiny under God. This was the spirit that infused the first scientists in ancient Greece; and eventually 2,500 years later, that led man into the EM Age. And today, as we approach A.D. 3000, our scientific and technologically affluent society, more than ever, guides itself by this principle. When it serves man's purpose to move a mountain, he should move it if he is able. Weather Control, like any immense problem, was to be "let well enough alone" when our knowledge of it was insufficient to conquer it. EM Science then gave man the knowledge. And Weather Control became a mountain to move.

The advance of Science forever feeds our appreciation of Nature and leads us closer to the Order of the Universe. And our progress in Science is paralleled by a deepening sense of personal accountability to this Order. As we gain an understanding of each Natural System—in this instance, of the Weather-Atmospheric Energy relationship—we have that awareness of our awesome responsibility to subordinate and harmonize man-made forces with the Natural forces, and not to upset the balance that Nature constantly demands. Our responsibility to preserve the balance of Nature is as urgent as our challenge to make the processes of Nature better servants of man.

By way of background—
A STUDY OF THE ADVERSARY AND THE FIELD OF BATTLE: THE ATMOSPHERE

The Sun's most beautiful and friendly planet, our Earth, wears a wondrous protective blanket over every inch of her body. Although the blanket is woven entirely of gases and vapors, its 200 miles of effective thickness load more than a ton onto each square foot of her terrestrial surface. Yet, Mother Earth complains little. For, if she were to shuck this atmospheric veil, this marvelous Natural filter against the deadly ultraviolet Solar radiations, her human children and all the other forms of life on Earth would soon vanish. Without her blanket of air, planet Earth's purpose in the Universe would become naught, as is the pitiful destiny of so many millions of her burned-out, lifeless fellow wanderers in the vastness of the celestial firmament.

Through the eons of time our transparent, translucent, life-providing Atmosphere has clung faithfully and tenaciously to Earth. How the other planets and even her Moon would love to steal some of this precious air from Earth. But Nature, a strict and orderly disciplinarian, that relentless enforcer of the physical laws, has seen to it that this specially designed blanket wears only the single label: "Made on and for planet Earth, to protect the life of her inhabitants—not for export."

Why we, rather than Mars or Venus or planets unknown, are blessed with this great gift, we may never really know. Of course, our Science Councils have come up with some mathematical and plausible—although equally unholy—explanations. But in a spirit of gratitude for our priceless endowment, we Earthlings willingly and unquestioningly accept the Atmosphere. The why and the how of it are secondary to the fact of our fortunate possession and prudent use of it.

We could hardly dream of a more fortuitous combination of chemistry than we find in our air. Its oxygen supports life so abundantly on the Earth's surface; and yet, 30 miles up in the chemosphere, this same oxygen, exposed to the brute force of the unfiltered Sun, spontaneously becomes poisonous ozone. Fortunately for us, the equally poisonous invading hordes of ultraviolet radiation expend themselves in the ozone-making process. And the impenetrable ozone curtains they have manufactured then block all the other ultraviolet battalions of the Sun from their Earthward march. It almost seems as though our "friendly" Atmosphere were following specific instructions to protect her Earthly wards.

Yet, as wonderful and as benevolent a performer as she is at times, there are other occasions when the Atmosphere is neither so kind, nor like a gentle spring lamb. She has her fits and turmoils. In fact, her cloudy lowest 10 miles—the troposphere, which make up 75% of her weight—is in a state of constant flux. We know that this internal strife of hers is just a method of effecting the balance of heat energies within herself—a balance that is so vital to her self-preservation. But this twisting and howling of her unstable air masses, the spiteful wet and dry tantrums, her sometimes scorching and other times freezing exploits have kept mankind in an "aweful" homage to her potential violence. Nonetheless, we do not want to appear unappreciative

or ever to invoke her scorn, because, on balance, we owe Miss
Atmosphere more than we could ever pay. So we refer politely
to her continuous changes in disposition as—weather.

Now don't jump to the conclusion, just because we say a
few nice things about her, that we are caught up in a reckless
love affair with this frivolous, hefty, "little lady." We are only
trying to be considerate of her stressful energy equilibrium situation, and to understand how it affects her personality. In the
long run, you know, there will be a limit to our patience and
to our tolerance of her grumbling. Then, when she cavorts beyond
those boundaries, when our patience has run out, we will want
to take judicious, carefully planned corrective action. Therefore,
for our own protection, we must look upon her as a potentially
high-swinging adversary, as well as a lovely lady.

Specifically, what is bothering her and provoking her into this
dual personality? It is really no secret. Every pair of eyes on
Earth sees him chasing her every day and watches as he unloads
his gigantic "gift" of Sunshine onto her and Mother Earth below.
That's right, it's that great big generous giant, our Sun, who
is responsible for Miss Atmosphere's energy-balance problem—
and for our Weather headaches. He's such a big guy—more than
a million times larger than Earth—and he has so much heat
energy to give away. On Earth we receive only one part out of
two billion (1/2,000,000,000th) that he radiates into space. Even
so, Mr. Sol shines down onto Mother Earth at the steady energy
rate of 10^{24} horsepower. In a single day his efforts amount to
a warming input of 6×10^{28} B.T.U., and in anybody's numbers
that is a lot of heat energy. Sun's daily input to Earth is, in fact,
10^{13} times greater than the total annual world generation of
electric energy. We can readily see—if we can comprehend the
exponential factors of the aforementioned astronomical numbers
—what a tremendous task the Atmosphere and the Earth's terrestrial surface have, to digest, distribute, and dispose of this daily
gift of Sunshine.

Energy cannot be destroyed. (Of course, we know that it
can be converted into mass—the reverse of the sun's energy-
making process—but then only under the strictest compliance

with natural physical laws and EM Scientific principles, and in conjunction with some very sophisticated machinery.) The energy-balance problem that confronts the Atmosphere and the terrestrial surface requires that every B.T.U. of this indestructible energy received from the Sun must be offset equally by energy radiated back into space. (We can neglect, in this broad consideration of energy balance, the relatively insignificant amount converted into sugar in the amazing process of plant photosynthesis. Because it is another "miracle" of Nature, we at least make this note of it.) If the energy-in and the energy-out balance is not achieved during Earth's daily, monthly, and yearly courses through the heavens, her various climatic zones will react as though their thermostats have run wild. Great areas of our planet would become ever-hotter uninhabitable ovens, or alternately, frigid iceboxes approaching true zero. So, when the Sun isn't looking, Earth and Atmosphere manage the net release of huge amounts of radiant energy—to keep the input-output score balanced. And of course, terrestrial radiation continues for 24 hours every day, while the sun gets only half that chance (on the yearly average) to contribute to the plus side of the ledger.

If generous Mr. Sun were able to place his shine in equal portions over all the area of the Earth, we would have neither great climatic differences nor violent Weather extremes. But Mother Nature writes the rules in this game. And even—in a parallel sense—as Nature gives and takes unequally of her human children, she distributes incoming Sunshine and outgoing terrestrial radiation without feeling or fairness. Certain areas receive more than they can use or even reject through radiation; and other zones of the Earth radiate more to space than they receive from the Sun. For example, a gross disproportion of Solar energy happens to be deposited onto the equatorial and tropical belts of Earth. And in the radiate-more-than-receive department, we know that the North and South Polar regions, which alternately endure six months of continuous night, are immense radiators of terrestrial heat, aided in this giveaway process by their snow-covered surfaces and by the relatively thin depths of insulting Atmosphere that exist on the top and bottom of the World.

The explanation for this unequal or "unfair" distribution of heat energy over the Earth's surface is neither mysterious nor metaphysical. A long list of specific, clearly explainable natural circumstances line themselves up in opposition to an equal areal distribution of the received, and also, of the re-radiated energies. Reason number one, blatantly obvious, is the global shape of Earth, which makes the incidence angle of Sunshine's rays progressively flatter as latitudes count from 0 to 90 degrees Northward and Southward toward the Poles. Earth's one-shoulder-low posture—the 23 degree inclination of the North-South axis—as it orbits the Sun in its annual voyage, is also a big factor in energy disproportionment and is the principal cause of our four seasons. Between the one extreme of her North Pole's 23-degree hunch away from the Sun during Northern Hemisphere winter, to the equal but opposite leaning, 23 degrees into the focus (Sun) of her elliptical orbit during the summer, Earth experiences a continual variation in the length of her days and nights in every location on her surface—except along the neutral equator. The greatest swing, as we know, is in the Polar regions where daytime and nighttime range alternately from non-existent to 24 hours long. In intermediate latitudes between the equator and poles, the seasonally controlled durations of day and night, with their related heating and cooling times, literally vary "all over the map." The geometry of our globe, and the inclined placement of the Earth on its track in the heavens inherently do not allow the heat balance problem to be a $2 + 2 = 4$ simplicity. And there are many other circumstances that confound the arithmetic even more. The changing cloud cover in every region is an inconstant energy filter that cannot be discounted. To this, add the uncertainty of energy in-and-out rates caused by variations in the physical features of the Earth's surface—land or sea, vegetable or mineral, bright reflective or black absorbent, liquid or frozen, rough or smooth.

Although it may appear that the cards are stacked against an orderly accounting of the energy books, Nature pursues the gigantic addition and subtraction task steadily and, even at times, with a vengeance. Her two stalwart transfer agents, Mr. Ocean Current and Miss Atmosphere, each pick up their share of the energy-balance assignment. Employing tons upon tons of the Earth's most abundant surface material—water—these two act as managers of the biggest energy distribution corporation ever dreamed of. In each pound of water that ocean current carries, there is a unit B.T.U. for each degree rise of its temperature. By sheer brute mass, but at the 1 B.T.U. per pound per degree F. rate, untold tons of ocean water move their cargo of heat energy away from the central latitudes toward colder regions where it can be exchanged to the Atmosphere or radiated directly off the books.

Above the ocean's surface, standing at least 10 miles tall and with absolutely no respect for shorelines or other earthly fences, the second manager, Miss Atmosphere, puts her shoulder to the wheel. Some observers say that Atmosphere is the brains of the team whereas Ocean Current represents the muscle. And these admirers are quite specific in backing their champion, stating that Atmosphere loads 1,000 more B.T.U.'s into each pound of water that she employs in this energy distribution business, than does Ocean Current. They are technically correct, for Atmosphere does capitalize on water's unique thermodynamic attribute, one that far exceeds this disposition in any other common material on Earth. This outstanding physical property of water is its ability to absorb an amazing 1,065 B.T.U.'s per pound evaporated from the liquid to the vapor state. By utilizing this sensational energy storage capacity (latent heat of evaporation) in each pound of water vapor, Miss Atmosphere successfully competes for managerial recognition against the massiveness of Mr. "1 B.T.U. per pound per degree F." Ocean Current.

Both energy distribution managers, however, constantly work together to help Nature preserve the energy status-quo upon Earth. Their clear-cut responsibility is to keep the surplus blocks of heat energy moving away from overheated tropics, toward the North and South circumpolar radiators. Enroute northward and southward from the equator, Atmosphere's thermodynamically loaded air masses, periodically drawing renewed strength from Ocean Current's moisture, invade the middle latitude blending zones. Here, amidst considerable stirring and agitation, the great exchange of enthalpies, the mixing of hot with cold, takes place. This dynamic manifestation of the globe-circling interchange of air mass energy is the phenomenon we call Weather—the very same cocktail that turns our lovely lady, Miss Atmosphere, into a growling tigress.

*   *   *

Our abbreviated attempt herein to explain the Atmosphere and its assignment in Nature is, because of our rough and callous oversimplification, an injustice to a profound subject. Many books, and indeed, many lifetimes, have been devoted to in-depth studies of this marvelous blanket that covers our Earth. But even a fragmentary awareness of the physical complications within the Atmosphere will serve to give us a respect for the Control of Weather—which, as one of the founding and enduring wonders of EM Technology, is our current and particular subject. We recognize that our man-made stimulative forces used in Weather Control are so pitifully small compared to the power in the Atmosphere. Yet, the calculated and timely use of Weather Control techniques introduces order and selection into the resolution of the same stability and energy-balance that Nature seeks. Man's control-valving of the Atmospheric heat exchanger permits him to conveniently schedule normal Weather variances and to prevent the build-up within air masses of those stressful enthalpies that tend toward violent solutions of severe tempest, or of oppressive stagnation.

The Control of Weather, even the very thought of it, is one of mankind's greatest challenges; but the rewards in terms of Weather moderation and Climatic improvement are beyond measure.

THE PIONEER WEATHER CONTROL STATION
WAMSUTTER, WYOMING, A.D. 2000

Two important and immediate challenges confronted the first EM scientists with their announcement in A.D. 1985 of history's

Veather Control, this pair came to be known as the "Work
ses of Wamsutter." And even today, our most modern W/C
ons are designed as arenas for this famous team—Rayforms
and #27.

Often called the Water Carrier Rayform, R-17 has the capa-
 to adsorb, carry, and desorb water vapor. Its partner in
ess, Rayform 27, is the prodigious Solar Radiation Adsorber.
's ability to adsorb not only solar ultraviolet energy but
the energies of the other spectrally related radiant waves
hich it can be tuned, and also its subsequent controllable
ability to the conversion of its adsorbed burdens into
on flat-wave direct current electricity (Rayform 10), have
d for the Solar Radiation Adsorber a recognition as being
widely known and best understood by our EM Age people.
ireless reception of Rayform 27 into the unitized electric
 cubicles of millions of homes and industrial facilities is
nmonplace application of Rayform 27 Technology. Its
te capability to transport and to convert adsorbed Solar
 directly into the sensible heat radiations is another of its
own services to man.

h of the work horse EM Rayforms were generated in the
C-M-A (Converter-Magnetizer-Accelerator) at Wamsutter.
ajectories of Rayforms 17 and 27 are totally manageable
mpletely shapeable—even to square corners—and are well
o the 10 mile high projection patterns used in Weather
. As specific burden carriers, Rayforms 17 and 27 were
together, actually interlaced in the airspace over the test
form a Weather Control "umbrella." In this 10 mile x 10
00-square-mile) deployment over the Red Desert of
g, the two Rayforms were then coordinated to effect
 of the several types of Weather problems, including
 (Solar) and outgoing (terrestrial) heat shielding, mois-
servation, rain inducement, and long-range climate modi-

der to gain a clear understanding of the team's technical
 at Wamsutter, let's look in detail first at R-17, the
rrier Rayform. We will study its origins, its adaptability

most amazing Scientific Breakthrough. The EM Discoveries, the
100 prodigious Rayforms, needed to be proved on large-scale,
practical applications outside the laboratory. And almost as
urgent as proof of the Rayforms' technical practicality was the
necessity to demonstrate the wonders of EM Rayform Technology
to the people of the World, in order to gain popular acceptance
of this new and startling scientific knowledge.

Pioneer EM scientists, wisely sensitive to the pulse of the day,
were quick to realize that a large-area Weather Control project
offered the opportunity to meet both challenges. They knew
that the many ramifications of Weather Control could serve as
a testing and proving ground for several of the new EM Rayforms.
A Weather Control project also offered, in the political sense,
the prospect of displaying on a grand scale a tangible product
of Rayform Technology, one that would illustrate the great potential for many additional environmental advancements that could
soon be working for all of mankind.

This time in history, the final quarter of the 20th century,
was a multiple crossroad for the human race. As an influence on
the social and political courses that world society would take
from that crossroad, EM Science played a crucial role. The
divergently motivated nations of the World direly needed a unifying
force, a common inspiration toward peaceful coexistence on Earth.
Continuance of inter-nation distrust and military rivalry, and the
almost certain channeling of virtually all scientific and technical
progress into the technology of weapons—with horrible destructive
capabilities—portended the recession of the human race. Concerned world leaders of that time, as well as the pioneer EM
scientists, hoped that the new EM Science and its Technologies
could be that unifying force for world peace.

WAMSUTTER, WYOMING—Latitude 41-40° North, Longitude 108-00° West, 800 miles inland from the Pacific Ocean,
7,000 feet above sea level, in the center of the Red Desert of
South Central Wyoming, annual rainfall less than 10 inches. This
ancient sheepherders station, on the Union Pacific Railroad's
plateau route through the North America Rockies, was chosen
to be the site of the first EM Weather Control installation. The

W/C (Weather Control) site was exactly 10 miles x 10 miles square, sectioned on the cardinal directions, with the town of Wamsutter marking the Southeast corner. Climate and terrain in the surrounding Red Desert were not unlike those in much of the semi-arid land of the World; and except for a lack of moisture, soil conditions were minerally and texturally suitable, although not "grade A" fertile, for agriculture. The Atmospheric air masses floating over Wamsutter normally were well-dehydrated by prior call on their moisture content during their passage over the mountains and dry lands of California, Nevada, and Utah. But even at the prevailing low relative humidity, there were always a few grains of water vapor remaining in each cubic foot of the stable Atmosphere over this desert plateau.

The plan at Wamsutter was to create narrow zones of artificial instability within the local air mass by Rayform injections of "imported" water vapor. And then, with the Atmosphere conditioned along these selected fronts, the unstable air would be provoked by Rayform trigger techniques to release small amounts (up to ½ inch) of rainfall. Meteorologists working with the pioneer EM scientists had determined that during Spring, Summer, and Autumn at least 5 inches of rainfall per month could be extracted from the stimulated air masses over the test site. Most of this precipitation would be taken during the evening hours, centering around sunset. During the growing season, from May to October, showers were scheduled to occur on 10 occasions each month, at intervals of 2, 3, or 4 days. Some variations in the timing of rainfalls were to be expected in order to take advantage of any natural instabilities and higher moisture contents of random crossing air masses. In the colder months, from November through April, precipitation would be limited to 2 inches per month; the Weather Control installation would operate principally to minimize Weather extremes and to conserve daytime's solar warming during the night hours.

The long-range goal at Wamsutter was to transform the site from a barren wasteland that for ages had hardly supported a dozen jackrabbits, into a 100-square mile farm equal in fertility and agricultural production to the best Muscatine loams of Iowa.

Livestock would thrive on lush green pastures in the test site would grow and harvest a fu rich grains. Within the first 10 years EM equally excited staff of agronomy experts also than 100,000 Cottonwoods, Sycamores, V Hickorys, and Chestnuts reaching for the sky country roadways. By the utilization of R and heat transfer techniques, summer clima intense, and in fact, would be extended a ends. The frost-free growing season at th would run from early May through Octob into the middle of November—an improv over normal climate conditions. Also, by form shielding techniques to retain da during the night hours, Winter would b average.

Wamsutter today, still in operation continuous improvements for close to 1 the early pioneers planned and dreame great basin of Wyoming, as well as h square miles of former wasteland in th western United States, are now unde Weather and Climate Control. It is farms of Wamsutter Station from those area of the Red Desert. Indeed, from extending hundreds of miles in every appears as one vast endless expanse forest, guarded by the ever-watching north and south.

TWO FAMOUS WORK HORSES

Nearly 50 of the newly discovere selves gainfully employed in the bu with the Weather Control program there were two principal and outsta their complementary adaptability to to Weather Control, and we will check its interesting related role in revolutionizing Water Supply. Next, we consider, also separately, the wondrous features of R-27 in its bold endeavor to regulate a "measurable" fraction of the immense power and energy that the Earth receives from the Sun. Then, in a combined analysis of the two as the work horses of Weather Control, we follow the team from Wamsutter through the emerging years of the EM Age, to study their part in the conquest of various Weather situations and to observe their technological assignments in the OMNI System, and in the Climate Improvement and Land Reclamation programs

RAYFORM 17—THE WATER CARRIER

Students of the early history of EM Weather Control are convinced that one of William Josephs' colleagues—or perhaps it was the great Discoverer himself—was a baseball enthusiast. The physical layout at Wamsutter is certainly patterned after the familiar baseball diamond, with the southeast town corner serving as home plate. First base is 10 miles due north, second base 10 miles west from that point—and around third and back home in equal legs. In programmed batting order, each of the Rayform 17 pulses takes its turn at the plate, gets a hit, and starts out toward first base. But here, in our analogy, strict adherence to the rules of baseball ceases. The technical mission of W/C Rayforms is not to circle the bases but to blanket the entire 100 square mile area within the baselines. Therefore, in rapid succession as they race down the first base line, the pulses break sharply from their low-level course, veer upward, 10 miles across and down onto the second-third base-line. Each pulse travels an incremental distance farther, in sprinting down the first base-line, before taking to the air across the infield. In this way a "solid" East to West raster of Rayform 17 lines thread through the sky to spin the Weather Control umbrella. With their speed-of-light velocity, all of the "runners" eventually round third base and head for home, for reloading and another trip. The controlled variations in their base running techniques and in their water vapor antics along the route are worth noting. And so, it may even help our analysis to agree that there could have been a baseball fan operating among the pioneer scientists— one who had quite an influence on the field layout and programming at Wamsutter.

Here are some ground-rule particulars concerning Rayform 17 Technology at the first Weather Control Station:

Source Material: Direct Current Energy (Rayform 10).

Most of the early Rayforms were derived from the substance of Rayform 10, the carrier of common D.C. Electricity. Rayform 10 exists and persists naturally in the environmental ambients of Earth. (It was not until A.D. 2200 that GRAVITY, stored in Gravitational Effect Condensers, was first used as a source *materia* for the constitution of Rayforms.)

Origin: The Wamsutter C-M-A.

Rayform 17 pulses were synthesized in the on-site C-M-A (Converter-Magnetizer-Accelerator) Equipment. The C-M-A at Wamsutter was an expanded version of the laboratory model in which William Josephs and the EM pioneers constituted the discovery Rayforms. Heavy structural and mechanical configurations were used in the early C-M-A's to establish cryogenic (near absolute zero) temperatures and to accelerate particles of D.C. electrical *materia* to the R-17 conversion velocity of Lach 1.01 (1.01 × the speed of light). These "unearthly" conditions are part of the staging required for constituting Rayforms (such as R-17) that do not persist naturally in our physical environment. The C-M-A at Wamsutter—even as in our modern C-M-A mobile package units—provided the "chamber of ambients" for a specific *materia* to undergo a transformation in relativity from Earth reference to Universal reference.

Persistence: 10 seconds.

At the water vapor loading rates used in Weather Control, Rayform 17 carriers have a useful persistence time of 10 seconds —usually expressed as 10^7 (10 million) micro-seconds. After most amazing Scientific Breakthrough. The EM Discoveries, the 100 prodigious Rayforms, needed to be proved on large-scale, practical applications outside the laboratory. And almost as urgent as proof of the Rayforms' technical practicality was the necessity to demonstrate the wonders of EM Rayform Technology to the people of the World, in order to gain popular acceptance of this new and startling scientific knowledge.

Pioneer EM scientists, wisely sensitive to the pulse of the day, were quick to realize that a large-area Weather Control project offered the opportunity to meet both challenges. They knew that the many ramifications of Weather Control could serve as a testing and proving ground for several of the new EM Rayforms. A Weather Control project also offered, in the political sense, the prospect of displaying on a grand scale a tangible product of Rayform Technology, one that would illustrate the great potential for many additional environmental advancements that could soon be working for all of mankind.

This time in history, the final quarter of the 20th century, was a multiple crossroad for the human race. As an influence on the social and political courses that world society would take from that crossroad, EM Science played a crucial role. The divergently motivated nations of the World direly needed a unifying force, a common inspiration toward peaceful coexistence on Earth. Continuance of inter-nation distrust and military rivalry, and the almost certain channeling of virtually all scientific and technical progress into the technology of weapons—with horrible destructive capabilities—portended the recession of the human race. Concerned world leaders of that time, as well as the pioneer EM scientists, hoped that the new EM Science and its Technologies could be that unifying force for world peace.

WAMSUTTER, WYOMING—Latitude 41-40⁰ North, Longitude 108-00⁰ West, 800 miles inland from the Pacific Ocean, 7,000 feet above sea level, in the center of the Red Desert of South Central Wyoming, annual rainfall less than 10 inches. This ancient sheepherders station, on the Union Pacific Railroad's plateau route through the North America Rockies, was chosen to be the site of the first EM Weather Control installation. The

W/C (Weather Control) site was exactly 10 miles x 10 miles square, sectioned on the cardinal directions, with the town of Wamsutter marking the Southeast corner. Climate and terrain in the surrounding Red Desert were not unlike those in much of the semi-arid land of the World; and except for a lack of moisture, soil conditions were minerally and texturally suitable, although not "grade A" fertile, for agriculture. The Atmospheric air masses floating over Wamsutter normally were well-dehydrated by prior call on their moisture content during their passage over the mountains and dry lands of California, Nevada, and Utah. But even at the prevailing low relative humidity, there were always a few grains of water vapor remaining in each cubic foot of the stable Atmosphere over this desert plateau.

The plan at Wamsutter was to create narrow zones of artificial instability within the local air mass by Rayform injections of "imported" water vapor. And then, with the Atmosphere conditioned along these selected fronts, the unstable air would be provoked by Rayform trigger techniques to release small amounts (up to ½ inch) of rainfall. Meteorologists working with the pioneer EM scientists had determined that during Spring, Summer, and Autumn at least 5 inches of rainfall per month could be extracted from the stimulated air masses over the test site. Most of this precipitation would be taken during the evening hours, centering around sunset. During the growing season, from May to October, showers were scheduled to occur on 10 occasions each month, at intervals of 2, 3, or 4 days. Some variations in the timing of rainfalls were to be expected in order to take advantage of any natural instabilities and higher moisture contents of random crossing air masses. In the colder months, from November through April, precipitation would be limited to 2 inches per month; the Weather Control installation would operate principally to minimize Weather extremes and to conserve daytime's solar warming during the night hours.

The long-range goal at Wamsutter was to transform the site from a barren wasteland that for ages had hardly supported a dozen jackrabbits, into a 100-square mile farm equal in fertility and agricultural production to the best Muscatine loams of Iowa.

Livestock would thrive on lush green pastures while cropland areas in the test site would grow and harvest a full variety of protein-rich grains. Within the first 10 years EM scientists and their equally excited staff of agronomy experts also hoped to have more than 100,000 Cottonwoods, Sycamores, Walnuts, burly-barked Hickorys, and Chestnuts reaching for the sky, shading the pleasant country roadways. By the utilization of Rayform heat shielding and heat transfer techniques, summer climates would become less intense, and in fact, would be extended a month longer on both ends. The frost-free growing season at that 7,000-foot elevation would run from early May through October, and sometimes even into the middle of November—an improvement of three months over normal climate conditions. Also, by employing similar Rayform shielding techniques to retain daytime solar input heat during the night hours, Winter would be 20 degrees milder on average.

Wamsutter today, still in operation and having undergone continuous improvements for close to 1,000 years, is everything the early pioneers planned and dreamed. Of course, the entire great basin of Wyoming, as well as hundreds of thousands of square miles of former wasteland in the contiguous areas of the western United States, are now under the OMNI System of Weather and Climate Control. It is difficult to distinguish the farms of Wamsutter Station from those in the adjacent reclaimed area of the Red Desert. Indeed, from the air, the entire region extending hundreds of miles in every direction from Wamsutter appears as one vast endless expanse of verdant farmland and forest, guarded by the ever-watching, distant moutains to the north and south.

TWO FAMOUS WORK HORSES

Nearly 50 of the newly discovered EM Rayforms found themselves gainfully employed in the budding technologies associated with the Weather Control program at Wamsutter. Of all the 50, there were two principal and outstanding performers. Because of their complementary adaptability to the basic technological tasks in Weather Control, this pair came to be known as the "Work Horses of Wamsutter." And even today, our most modern W/C stations are designed as arenas for this famous team—Rayforms #17 and #27.

Often called the Water Carrier Rayform, R-17 has the capability to adsorb, carry, and desorb water vapor. Its partner in harness, Rayform 27, is the prodigious Solar Radiation Adsorber. R-27's ability to adsorb not only solar ultraviolet energy but also the energies of the other spectrally related radiant waves to which it can be tuned, and also its subsequent controllable adaptability to the conversion of its adsorbed burdens into common flat-wave direct current electricity (Rayform 10), have earned for the Solar Radiation Adsorber a recognition as being most widely known and best understood by our EM Age people. The wireless reception of Rayform 27 into the unitized electric power cubicles of millions of homes and industrial facilities is a commonplace application of Rayform 27 Technology. Its alternate capability to transport and to convert adsorbed Solar energy directly into the sensible heat radiations is another of its well-known services to man.

Both of the work horse EM Rayforms were generated in the on-site C-M-A (Converter-Magnetizer-Accelerator) at Wamsutter. The trajectories of Rayforms 17 and 27 are totally manageable and completely shapeable—even to square corners—and are well suited to the 10 mile high projection patterns used in Weather Control. As specific burden carriers, Rayforms 17 and 27 were teamed together, actually interlaced in the airspace over the test site, to form a Weather Control "umbrella." In this 10 mile x 10 mile (100-square-mile) deployment over the Red Desert of Wyoming, the two Rayforms were then coordinated to effect solutions of the several types of Weather problems, including incoming (Solar) and outgoing (terrestrial) heat shielding, moisture conservation, rain inducement, and long-range climate modification.

In order to gain a clear understanding of the team's technical functions at Wamsutter, let's look in detail first at R-17, the Water Carrier Rayform. We will study its origins, its adaptability

to Weather Control, and we will check its interesting related role in revolutionizing Water Supply. Next, we consider, also separately, the wondrous features of R-27 in its bold endeavor to regulate a "measurable" fraction of the immense power and energy that the Earth receives from the Sun. Then, in a combined analysis of the two as the work horses of Weather Control, we follow the team from Wamsutter through the emerging years of the EM Age, to study their part in the conquest of various Weather situations and to observe their technological assignments in the OMNI System, and in the Climate Improvement and Land Reclamation programs

RAYFORM 17—THE WATER CARRIER

Students of the early history of EM Weather Control are convinced that one of William Josephs' colleagues—or perhaps it was the great Discoverer himself—was a baseball enthusiast. The physical layout at Wamsutter is certainly patterned after the familiar baseball diamond, with the southeast town corner serving as home plate. First base is 10 miles due north, second base 10 miles west from that point—and around third and back home in equal legs. In programmed batting order, each of the Rayform 17 pulses takes its turn at the plate, gets a hit, and starts out toward first base. But here, in our analogy, strict adherence to the rules of baseball ceases. The technical mission of W/C Rayforms is not to circle the bases but to blanket the entire 100 square mile area within the baselines. Therefore, in rapid succession as they race down the first base line, the pulses break sharply from their low-level course, veer upward, 10 miles across and down onto the second-third base-line. Each pulse travels an incremental distance farther, in sprinting down the first base-line, before taking to the air across the infield. In this way a "solid" East to West raster of Rayform 17 lines thread through the sky to spin the Weather Control umbrella. With their speed-of-light velocity, all of the "runners" eventually round third base and head for home, for reloading and another trip. The controlled variations in their base running techniques

and in their water vapor antics along the route are worth noting. And so, it may even help our analysis to agree that there could have been a baseball fan operating among the pioneer scientists— one who had quite an influence on the field layout and programming at Wamsutter.

Here are some ground-rule particulars concerning Rayform 17 Technology at the first Weather Control Station:

Source Material: Direct Current Energy (Rayform 10).

Most of the early Rayforms were derived from the substance of Rayform 10, the carrier of common D.C. Electricity. Rayform 10 exists and persists naturally in the environmental ambients of Earth. (It was not until A.D. 2200 that GRAVITY, stored in Gravitational Effect Condensers, was first used as a source *materia* for the constitution of Rayforms.)

Origin: The Wamsutter C-M-A.

Rayform 17 pulses were synthesized in the on-site C-M-A (Converter-Magnetizer-Accelerator) Equipment. The C-M-A at Wamsutter was an expanded version of the laboratory model in which William Josephs and the EM pioneers constituted the discovery Rayforms. Heavy structural and mechanical configurations were used in the early C-M-A's to establish cryogenic (near absolute zero) temperatures and to accelerate particles of D.C. electrical *materia* to the R-17 conversion velocity of Lach 1.01 (1.01 × the speed of light). These "unearthly" conditions are part of the staging required for constituting Rayforms (such as R-17) that do not persist naturally in our physical environment. The C-M-A at Wamsutter—even as in our modern C-M-A mobile package units—provided the "chamber of ambients" for a specific *materia* to undergo a transformation in relativity from Earth reference to Universal reference.

Persistence: 10 seconds.

At the water vapor loading rates used in Weather Control, Rayform 17 carriers have a useful persistence time of 10 seconds —usually expressed as 10^7 (10 million) micro-seconds. After

10^7 micro-seconds, the velocity of propogation of a Rayform 17 pulse decreases rapidly—at an exponential rate proportional to the amount of water vapor loading.

Initial Velocity: 186,000 miles per second, the speed of light.

Rayform 17 pulse blocks constituted in the C-M-A- are furnished to the water vapor loading station with Lach 1 (speed of light) velocity characteristic. At nominal W/C water vapor loading rates, R-17 pulses retain a satisfactory velocity for their full persistence time.

SOME TIMING CONSIDERATIONS

——MILLI, MICRO, NANO, and PICO

At this point in our analysis of R-17 and Weather Control, we should digress a moment to review our concept of that fundamental unit of measurements—Time. Time is recognized by everyone as the fourth dimension. But, in describing objects in motion at known velocities—such as Rayforms, P.M.I. aerospace vessels, and Cosmic Bodies,—time units are also used to express the first three dimensions, which, of course, are length, width, and depth. Thus, in the macro sense, we use the timing descriptive, Light-Year (and its positive exponential multiples), to represent distances of great length, width, or depth. Galactic measurements, as an example, would be cumbersome if not stated in macro *time* units. And as we approach the opposite sense, the micro sphere of relativity, we must deal with time units, in all four dimensions, that are small beyond human comprehension. It is in this micro sense of the timing dimensionals that the parameters of Rayform Technology find practical expression.

Ancient 20th-century electronic technicians were among the first to recognize that the usual notations of time, those tied to the human pace, had limitations in scientific and technical expression. In their achievements in Radar Electronics, these immediate forerunners of the EM Age popularized the use of a new system of miniature-time expression. Their milli-, micro-, nano-, and pico-second time units have carried over to become part of the standard language of Rayforms. From their respective numerical multiples of 10^{-3}, 10^{-6}, 10^{-9}, and 10^{-12} we can see that there are 1,000 micro's in a milli, 1,000 nano's in a micro, and 1,000 pico's in a nano. Or we can say that each of the miniature cardinals is 1/1,000 times smaller than its predecessor, and 1/1,000,000 times smaller than its second predecessor—aiding in the over-all comprehensibility.

By using micro and nano time units in Rayform-propagation reference, we can simplify and clarify numerical values of velocity, acceleration, and distance. The usual velocity of light, Lach 1 or 186,00 miles per second, now has equivalent expression as 1,116 feet per micro-second, or 1.116 feet per nano-second. And conversely, a nano-second of length (for an object traveling at the speed of light) equals 1.116 feet, a measure that easily fits into the mind's eye. Pico-second (10^{-12}) timing, the most diminutive of the cardinals, makes an absurdity of vel-acc-dist measurements even at the fantastic speed of light. However, with the advancement by the year A.D. 2500 into the P.M.I. (Projected Magnetic Image) Propulsion capability of Lach 10^3 or 1,000 times the speed of light, pico-second timing became a practical reference level for velocities and accelerations assigned to interstellar voyages. (More of this interesting aspect of 26th-century technology in a later chapter dealing with P.M.I. (Projected Magnetic Image) Propulsion and celestial colonization.)

Well, so much for the pre-game briefing of milli, micro, nano, and pico. And just in time, too, because the umpire is about to signal, "Play Ball!" So let's focus back to Wamsutter's 10-mile-square ball diamond to observe how these micro-time cardinals are used to weave the Weather Control umbrella—and to keep the score.

FOLLOWING A RAYFORM 17 PULSE AROUND THE W/C CIRCUIT

The phenomenal base-running expedition of each Rayform 17 pulse, and the multiple possible combinations of its parameters in the W/C program illustrate R-17's great range of control—

an accommodating characteristic of many of the 100 EM Ray-forms. In considering its control-capability in W/C Technology, it will help us to look at R 17's A-B-C parameters—its principal descriptives expressed as functions of time. Keeping in mind that we are dealing with velocities of 186,000 miles/second, let's follow an R-17 pulse having W/C's nominal parameter A (pulse burden-length) of 120 micro-seconds. Parameter A, which defines the length of the Rayform that is loaded with water vapor, can be varied, in W/C Technology, between 20 and 200 micro-seconds. And let's classify our average pulse as also operating at the B and C nominals corresponding to a 100% operating power level. These value are: 5 nano-seconds in parameter B, outgoing main (first base line) gating; and 10 nano-seconds in parameter C, the timing interval between pulse initiations from home plate.

Parameter B (first base line gating) establishes the spacing between the east-west overhead raster lines. On our 10-mile, 60,000-foot-long trip down the first base line, this gating para-meter thus determines the total number of Rayform 17 "umbrella threads." The nominal gating of 5 nano-seconds establishes 10,800 east-west raster lines, separated on 5 nano-second or 5.55 foot centers. Parameter B can be varied between 2 and 100 nano-seconds, giving line totals from an idling or probing set-up of only 540 lines, up to a fine and maximum coverage of 27,000 lines.

Parameter C, the pulse timing interval, is the elapsed period between the starting instant (firing) of each successive pulse. Nominal 10 nano-second pulse firing interval means that 100 million pulses are initiated per second, each one following its predecessor's starting instant by 10 nano-seconds. In a pulse inter-val sense, the east-west raster lines may be concentrated from a dense 5 nano-second firing interval to a loose 1,000 nano-second interval. Although the values of these time periods—and lengths —sometimes appear to be out of man's range of comprehension, they nevertheless are real numbers representing finite measure-ments. As such they are suitable input notations for the W/C computer—which, of course, is not bothered by a comprehension problem.

Any combination of the A-B-C parameters is possible, within the energy and power capabilities of the station equipment. In addition to these three variables, the vertical height of the east-west lines can be regulated between 1,116 feet (1 micro-second) and 60,000 feet (54 micro-seconds) altitude, with slope-shaping up, across, and down on their paths. Slope-shaping enables W/C managers to synthesize Weather frontals, which in turn are strategically deployed to stimulate precipitation from the casual air masses that pass over the station. Synthesized frontals are employed to solve a variety of Weather situations. One interesting example is the case of smog-ladened inversions, where the frontals are used to stir and to impart forward motion to the 1,000 cubic-mile air volume over a Local 10 × 10-W/C station, in order to break up atmospheric stagnation caused by inverse-density layering.

NOW THAT HE HAS SOME ATTRIBUTES, LET'S SEE HOW HE RUNS

Our typical Rayform 17 pulse, characterized by 5 nano-second base line gating (B) and 10 nano-second pulse firing interval (C), and flying across the field at 10-mile altitude, will complete its circuit back to home plate in 270 micro-seconds, having traveled an average distance of 50 miles. On signal it will have released the water vapor load from its "burden-modulated" 120 micro-second length. (Water vapor release can be concentrated in a cumulative dumping at a frontal line, or it can be desorbed instantly and uniformly all along its burden length). Then, by allowing a safe recharging (water vapor adsorption) time of 250 micro-seconds, and an idle time of 500 micro-seconds in the "batter's circle" awaiting refiring, the total time expended per circuit by a Rayform pulse block will be about 1,000 micro-seconds. At its inherent persistence time of 10 seconds (10,000,000 micro-seconds), each block can be counted on to make 10,000 working trips before being shunted back to the C-M-A for reconstitution. Obviously, the station computer keeps quite busy, watching the aging cycles and counting the trips of each one of the thousands of pulse blocks simultaneously playing the ball game.

It is also interesting to note that the total time for a complete home plate to first base gating sequence—at the nominal parameters—is 108 micro-seconds (10,800 lines @ 10 nano-second firing intervals). And during the time (270 micro-seconds) that it takes for an average pulse block to make its 50 mile circuit, there will be some 27,000 pulse blocks operating concurrently. In each full second of operation, this constant population of 27,000 water-bearing R-17 pulses will trace a distance of 50 billion miles —or, in "astronomical" figures, a distance of 1 light-year (6×10^{12} miles) during each two minutes, within the squared confines of our 10-mile by 10-mile W/C site.

THE CORNER THAT ISN'T

Just in case you are wondering about the capability of a Rayform traveling at the speed of light to make a 90° caper, a sudden right angle change in course—as it does five times in rounding the W/C bases—without suffering attenuation of its velocity; be assured that you have wondered-up a worthy, but an explainable observation. EM Science shows us that a Rayform block, consisting of the basic carrier and its adsorbed burden, is composed of substantive, particulate matter. But the mass— or if you prefer, the inertia—of an EM Rayform and of its usual and practical quantity of adsorbed burden *materia*, even for a 186,000 mile (one-second) length, is infinitely small. And in relation to the material densities characteristic of the ambients of planet Earth, the mass of a working Rayform block—both the naturally occurring and the synthesized—is negligible. Therefore, Rayform blocks in Weather Control and in most other EM Technologies can be regarded (in Earth reference) as not possessing inertia. Because of this physical freedom, Rayforms know no such word as *corner* and show no centrifugal effect or measurable loss of velocity as a consequence of making sharp turns. Attesting to this phenomenon are the reflective properties of ordinary light, the constant velocity of common electricity in a meandering wire, and, of course, the constancy of radio propagation both within feed lines and in its efficient reflection from the "brick wall" magnetic *D, E,* and *F* layers of the ionosphere.

[The usual and practical burden-loading densities found in Nature—and normally employed in our EM Technologies—are consistent with and establish the inertial freedom of Rayform blocks. Deliberately overloaded Rayform blocks, however, do not qualify for the inertia-free state and suffer an attenuation in their propagation velocity corresponding to the loaded density of their adsorbed burdens. We shall observe this uncommon, though physically possible situation of burden overload in a subsequent review of pioneer Rayform 17 water pumping installations. In particular, the story of the Pacific Water Supply System—where a 1,000 times overload in R-17 burden density was accepted as a design compromise—illustrates the limitation of the inertia-free state of Rayforms.]

MILLIONS OF UMBRELLAS—
ONE FOR EVERY OCCASION

The preceding Rayform 17 description and performance detail, a verbal translation of a small fraction of the data stored in the memory cavities of Wamsutter's (or any W/C station's) program computer, represents only one combination of parameters. Thousands of combinations are possible. Remember, too, that Rayform 17 is not alone in the W/C umbrella. Its work horse partner, Rayform 27—the Infrared Adsorber—has an equal range of control. As a team, the two offer more than a million options in the shaping of the W/C umbrella. It is safe to say that even at pioneer Wamsutter—just as there are today in the thousands of OMNI System Weather Control Stations—there were an infinite number of R-17 and R-27 program combinations, each one best suited to a determinate weather condition and its corresponding solution.

RAYFORM 17's MOST VALUABLE AND UNIQUE
CAPABILITY
WATER VAPOR LOADING

R-17's marvelous base-running abilities, in themselves, cannot produce a drop of rainfall or even a cooling breeze. But Rayform

17, when loaded with energy-latent water vapor, can produce cloud bursts from the heavens and stir up wild winds on command. Its unique capability—as an extraordinary grant from Nature—to accept the substantive modulation of water vapor onto itself, the carrier, is without question the outstanding physical empowerment of the Water Carrier Rayform. It is a point both unique and remarkable in EM Science that Water Vapor is the only material *compound* in Nature that adapts itself to Rayform modulation (adsorption); and this, only onto the favored Rayform 17.

[There are only four other "heavy" material substantives that adapt to Rayform modulation, and these are all elementals: Hydrogen and Helium load onto Rayform 18, and the gaseous halogens, Fluorine and Chlorine, can be adsorbed onto Rayform 19. The bulk of the 100 Rayforms can only carry what we refer to as the attributes of *materia;* those intangible descriptives—real only in a relative context—such as temperature, pressure, solubility, hardness, magnetics, motion dynamics, and the many other physical "signs" that illustrate the circumstantial and environmental *status* of *materia.* More on this fascinating insight into EM Science is provided in a later essay dealing with the Technology of P.M.I. (Projected Magnetic Image) Propulsion and with the Periodic Table of the 100 Rayforms.]

As an aid in understanding the water vapor loading phenomenon of Rayform 17, we can consider the specific technological parallel—though it is in a greatly diminished mass-capability comparison—of voice-intelligence modulation of ordinary radio-frequency carriers (Rayforms 11 through 15). The common ground in an analogy of water vapor modulation to audio-intelligence modulation is that both, like light itself, are substantive; and, in the context of a relative and suitable environment, both of their modulation burdens possess mass. Radio carriers accept their loading via any of several electronic schemes; such as the modification of the base carrier by a heterodyning (algebraic summation) change of its amplitude, frequency, or pulsing characteristic. Rayform modulation, though basically analogous in end result, is accomplished via a much more complex and "out of this world" extension of technology. Adsorptive or superficial burden-loading—for the majority of EM Rayforms—can be achieved only under environmental ambients of temperature, pressure, and relative velocities far outside the normal range of our Earthly physicals. Cryogenic temperature conditions, densities approaching the neutron level, and compounded velocity rates—accelerations that lead to greater than Lach 1 velocity—all of these environmental states are required to constitute and to load burdens onto those Rayforms that are characteristically "not of our world." EM Science and Technology has given man the facility of the C-M-A (Converter-Magnetizer-Accelerator) wherein to accomplish for periods of up to 10 seconds the constitution of Rayforms and to condition them for the adsorption of substantive and attributive burdens.

For the purpose of our present explanatory analogy—without getting too involved in EM Scientific fundamentals at this time—it serves to note that both in Radio Technology (itself a Rayform application) and in Water Vapor Loading onto Rayform 17, the burdens are substantive. However, Water Vapor Loading rates per an R-17 unit pulse length can be 10^6 times greater than the audio-intelligence burden loading onto an equivalent length of Radio carrier. This remarkable difference in the degree of their burden-mass capabilities emphasizes the wonder of Water Vapor Loading—which is Rayform 17's most valuable and unique capability.

SUCCESS IN NUMBERS

In spite of its championship honors as a big weight lifter, Rayform 17, particularly on Weather Control assignment, transports an extremely small measure of water per unit Rayform block. The success of W/C Technology lies in the deployment of millions of unit carrier blocks each second. Nominal deployment at Wamsutter, as noted, is 27,000 concurrent pulse blocks during the average 270 micro-second circuit time. In a full second of time, there will be 100,000,000 total pulse blocks traveling the bases; with one block leaving the circuit and a new one taking its place each 10 nano-seconds. The great size of the army multiplies the insignificance of the unit burden into a product that indeed has measure.

In the water vapor loading station adjacent to the C-M-A building at Wamsutter, each Rayform 17 pulse adsorbs from the pool the almost immeasurable amount of 1/100 grain (1/700,000 pound) of water for each micro-second (1,116 feet) of its burden length. W/C station operation, at the 120 micro-second burden length and other nominal program parameters, requires a power input of 10,000 KW. This power level produces a total adsorption, each second, onto the 100,000,000 carriers equal to 120×10^6 grains—or its equivalent, 2,060 gallons per second. Net injection (desorption) into the atmosphere over the station, at the expected 97 percent system efficiency, is a round 2,000 gallons per second.

An arithmetical extension of the 2,000 gallons per second water vapor rate, at nominal 10,000 KW operating level, to its equivalent of 120,000 gallons per minute or 7,200,000 gallons per hour, gives us a more ponderable figure. Although the hourly rate now appears to represent no small measure of water, it still amounts to an insignificant quantity when related to the 100-square mile area that it must service as an air mass destabilizer and rain inducer. 7,200,000 gallons spread evenly over the test site would only wet the soil with 1/300 inch of rain, if such a small shower could be gauged. In practice, the Weather Control managers at Wamsutter aimed for timely injections into the atmosphere, for durations of one half-hour, to create meteorological conditions of "absolute instability" in susceptible local air masses. Their goal was either the consequent spontaneous, or a triggered precipitation of the atmosphere's naturally existing water vapor. This half-hour program of W-V injection called for an area-wide (100 square mile) expenditure of 1/600 inch of water in anticipation of ½ inch of rainfall; an investment of 1 part for a return of 300 parts.

WATER SUPPLY PROBLEMS

Water was the principal raw-material input as well as the basic end product—in the form of rainfall—at the pioneer W/C Station. To ensure the continuous operational availability of Wamsutter's facilities, it was necessary to maintain a water supply equal to a 10-hour demand of the Rayform 17 water vapor carriers, operating at the system designed power level of 10,000 KW. This water supply at Wamsutter was contained in a 1,000 × 1,000 × 10-foot deep pool located adjacent to the C-M-A building. During normal Controlled Weather periods, with their dependable one-half inch rainfalls every third or fourth day, there was no problem in keeping the 23 acre, 10,000,000 cubic foot reservoir fully stocked. Each rainfall blessed the site with an average of 150,000,000 cubic feet of new water; and the one-half million cubic feet used to produce the shower was easily replaced to the storage pool. At other times, however, during extended periods of extreme air-mass dryness or during the Springtime start-up schedule, when 6- to 8-inch per month rainfall rates were scheduled after the dry Winter season, there were frequent heavy demands on the station's water supply. On these occasions Wamsutter was not always self-sustaining, and water had to be pumped in from outside sources.

At the dawn of the EM Age, it was the order of the day to solve technical problems relating to EM projects with EM Technology itself. And so, the remarkable water-carrying capability of Rayform 17 was put to work, in a long distance pumping application, to solve the water supply problem. Nearest water to the test site was at Green River, Wyoming, 100 miles to the west. Here a temporary pumping station was set up on the mountain-fed stream that gives the town its name. This small pumping facility, consisting of a miniature C-M-A and a Rayform 17 A. & P.P. (Adsorption and Pulse Projection) Unit, easily transported its designed 1,000 gallons per minute over the aerial arch from the Green River to Wamsutter. But frequently, it was necessary to schedule pumping around the clock in order to meet the water demands of the test site. At seasonal times, the pump took a significant volume from the Green River, and it was obvious that a more reliable, year-round source of water was required.

THE PACIFIC WATER SUPPLY SYSTEM

A bold and far-reaching plan to deliver Wamsutter's air-mass charging water was placed into construction in the early days of the Weather Control Program. Because of the broad geographic scope of this undertaking, and the novelty of its engineering concepts, more than twenty years of construction and development were required for its completion. This significant project of pioneer times, which served both the W/C Program and the advancement of related EM technologies, was known as the Pacific Water Supply System.

Tapping the Pacific Ocean near Eureka in northern California, 800 miles west of Wamsutter, the Eureka Ocean Station—dedicated in A.D. 2005—pumped 14,500 gallons per minute; converting this 60 ton per minute load into Rayform 17 water vapor burden, and projecting it at the speed of light on its eastward, inland journey. In addition to the C-M-A and the compact 1,000 KW Rayform 17 A. & P. P. Unit at Eureka, a small EM Elemental Separator—another of the wondrous new Rayform processes—complemented the operation. Eureka's Elemental Separator extracted most of the ocean salts from the burden and fed only clean, fresh water into the Rayform 17 A. & P. P. Unit.

Water vapor loading rates used in early Rayform pumping installations were much greater than the adsorption rates assigned to Rayform 17 carriers operating in the Weather Control scheme. In fact, the 10-grain nominal burden density at Eureka Station was 1,000 times more than the 1/100 grain loading (per microsecond length) used in W/C Technology. This very dense loading onto continuously modulated carriers permitted pumping systems to operate with less than 2,500 R-17 carriers, compared to the nominal 27,000 concurrent blocks in a W/C umbrella. Use of this minimal number of carriers in pumping service resulted in a conservative investment in C-M-A equipment, and in a very low Pulse Projection cost.

But dense water vapor loading was not without its price, that of carrier attenuation with corresponding water vapor saturation and dew-pointing after only 100 miles of travel. Even in a 100-mile projection, the heavy loading rate caused water vapor losses of close to 2% of gross cargo. Any extension beyond 100 miles would have resulted in prohibitive spontaneous desorption. The over-all Pacific System design, therefore, called for relay stations at 100 trajectorial-mile intervals, where the heavily loaded Rayform 17 carrier could receive propulsion boosts back up to light velocity.

Seven intermediate relay locations were selected between Eureka Ocean Station and Wamsutter. The first inland station was north of Redding, California, on the eastern slope of Mount Shasta. Other relays, reminiscent of the old time Pony Express stops, were built at Cedarville, California, high in the Warner Range of the Rockies; and in Nevada at Winnemucca and Elko. Continuing eastward into Utah, stations at 100 trajectorial-mile intervals were constructed near Bonneville Flats and northeast of Ogden. The final relay station was located at Green River, Wyoming, on the site of the temporary 1,000-gallon per minute water supply facility.

Each inland relay station had a 10,000,000 cubic foot storage reservoir similar to the 23-acre × 10-foot deep supply pool at Wamsutter. When the water supply demands of the Weather Control Station had been satisfied, the seven relay stations, in turn, desorbed water from the Pacific Pumping System to stock their own pools. Each station had full 1,000 kw Adsorption-Desorption and Pulse Projection facilities, which could be used to deliver the locally stored water to the Weather Control Station in the event of equipment breakdown at the Ocean Pumping Station. The reliability of the Pacific Pumping System improved rapidly after the first few years of operation, assuring a surplus and dependable supply of fresh water for all points along the route. The fresh ocean water, needless to say, was most welcome in the relay station areas, particularly in the Nevada and Utah desert location. At the Pacific System's 12,000-gallon-per-minute net pumping rate, a four and one-half day pumping period filled each reservoir. In total, the seven relay stations and Wamsutter had a storage capacity of 80,000,000 cubic feet of water—a considerable quantity, but in comparison, only a little more than half the volume of water that a ½ inch rainfall would bring to the 10-mile × 10-mile Wamsutter Weather Control area.

The completion of the Pacific Water Supply and Pumping System in A.D. 2005 ensured a full and successful schedule at Wamsutter. This pipeless, frictionless method of transporting large volumes of water at less than 10% of the cost of conventional pumping methods marked the beginning of an important "sidelight" technology for Rayform 17. Within the 21st century, based on the engineering experience gained from the Pacific System, Rayform 17 Pumping Technology expanded into countless thousands of projects, delivering clean, fresh water in virtually unlimited volumes to many urban and other water-short areas of the world.

In our modern times the basic design of pumping plants is still similar to those of Eureka and her seven Relays. Today, however, with the cost of C-M-A equipment no longer a factor, and because of the facility of the constitution of Rayform 17 carriers from GRAVITY source *materia,* pumping systems can be designed that are attenuation-free and are operated without the loss of a drop of water. Rayform 17 Water Delivery Systems in almost any size, and capable of single trajectory projections from 100 to 10,000 miles, are now, in the 30th century, simply a matter of design choice and application.

RAYFORM 27
SOLAR INFRARED RADIATION ADSORBER, REFLECTOR, POWER CARRIER

The second, but by no means the lesser work horse at Wamsutter Weather Control Station, was Rayform 27, in itself, a sub-wonder of the EM age. With its pioneer assignment as the dense north-south warp threads in the W/C umbrella, Rayform 27 began serving mankind, as it so notably continues to do today, by bringing vital power, heat, and light into every household and productive enterprise of our civilization. No other single Rayform can match the multiplicity and generosity of R 27's direct benefits to humanity. In some manner, Rayform 27 touches and serves every person on Earth during almost every moment of time.

The story of Rayform 27 in Weather Control does more than tell of the technological versatility of this amazing EM carrier. Its role as Solar Radiation Adsorber shocks us into the reality of man's insignificance as a consumer of energy and a manipulator of physical force. When we consider the wondrous capability of EM Rayform 27 in its taming, harnessing, and transformation of the energy of the Sun, we cannot help but stand in respectful awe and amazement at the Power of the Universe, of the Creator.

Incoming Sunshine energy deposited onto the 100 square miles at Wamsutter W/C Station—as well as onto all middle latitude 100 square mile areas that see direct sunlight—arrives at a midday average power level of 450,000,000 Kw, or approximately 1⅛ KW per square yard of surface. This rate of Solar energy impingement onto only a 10-mile by 10-mile square is twice as much as America's total electrical generating capacity in the late 20th century. Rayform 27's bold and monumental task at Wamsutter was to "influence" this huge block of incoming energy by Adsorbing or Reflecting up to 10% of its infrared radiations. The degree (up to 10% maximum) and the direction of its influence were tactical choices of Wamsutter's Weather Control managers.

Of the two directive techniques, Adsorption and Reflection, the former found the majority of application. Adsorption technology was employed, for example, to break up Sunlight-blocking stratified cloud layers, or to promote vertical lifting of moisture-containing air masses. In these processes, Rayform 27 carriers modulated to Adsorb, were patterned at 8- to 10-mile altitudes, above the blanketing clouds, where they captured incoming infrared energy. The Adsorbed burden was then carried into specific zones within the lower, clouded levels for re-insertion as heat, to effect an expansion and movement in the problem air mass. Dynamic heat-energy reinsertions, along frontal lines, were frequently used in the creation of rain-making "instabilities" within local air masses. Adsorption techniques also could be applied, at the lower elevations, to extract heat from clear and cloudless air, lowering temperatures enough to reach dew point condition. In this manner protective cloud covers were produced when there was a need to shield the underlying terrain from excessive heating or evaporation. This low-level Adsorption method of synthesizing clouds found popular application during the night-times of early Spring and late Autumn, to suppress terrestrial heat radiation and to prevent damaging ground frosts.

The Reflection modulation mode of Rayform 27 found its calling in Weather Control during atmospheric circumstances that proved too great a task for the Adsorption mode. Hot and cloudless mid-summer days, with their very dry air condition, defied Adsorption techniques. Heat captured by Adsorption was usually utilized to change the state of the casual water vapor present in the local air mass—in a thermodynamic solution of the Weather situation. But without sufficient atmospheric moisture, or in ambients that precluded the efficient addition of Rayform 17 water vapor, the Adsorption mode of Rayform 27 was ineffective. Under these adverse conditions, R-27 Reflection was called into service to relieve the scorched Earth. Deployed as a "bright-reflective" umbrella at maximum 10-mile altitude, Infrared Reflection was able to turn 10% of the Sun's incoming energy back out to space.

From Wamsutter's C-M-A corner, Rayform 27 carriers were projected into aerial cover over the W/C site by pulse-firing and gating systems similiar to those of R-17, the water vapor work horse. Rayform 27, however, ran the bases backward; if we can recall our baseball analogy. The Infrared Adsorber's overhead raster began from the third base gating line. And its south to north paths were very closely spaced—60,000 lines nominal compared to R-17's 10,800 east to west lines. Rayform 27's closely knit south to north raster was required to intercept the "solid front" of incoming Sunlight.

A VALUABLE BY-PRODUCT
—RAYFORM 27, THE MOONLIGHTER

Rayform 17 and 27 as a team produced the Weather Control Station's two principal products: the intangible achievement of local Weather moderation, and the very tangible product—rainwater. Rayform 27, moreover, was not content with just its W/C assignment; it kept doubly busy during the 24 hours of every day, manufacturing its famous by-product, Electricity. Actually, the transformation of its Adsorption-mode infrared burden into Rayform 10 (common D.C. Electricity) was a convenient way to unload; so that it could remain in cycle and return into the W/C umbrella to perform its primary mission of gathering more infrared energy. Adsorption modes were always favored by W/C mangers because of the wide margin for plant efficiency that Adsorption offered over the Reflection mode of operation. The latter required considerable energy input, and of course, the carriers returned empty from their blocking, Reflective mission.

It is a matter of record that Rayform 27's contribution of electric energy to the Rocky Mountain Edison System more than returned the cost of operation of the Wamsutter W/C Station. In addition to the electric energy sold to the utility system, R-27's valuable by-product furnished more than 90% of the Kilowatt-Hour consumption of the W/C facility. Reflection mode operation was the only program, except for seasonal start-up or an occasional equipment breakdown, which caused a negative or reverse flow of electric energy into the Station.

SOME POWER CONSIDERATIONS
R-27's 1/10th of 1%

It was the usual practice at Wamsutter test site—as it is even today in our OMNI Weather Control Stations—to maintain a full Rayform 27 raster in continuous 24-hour deployment. R-27's 60,000 screening lines could be modulated in groups or individually, to either of the two modes (Adsorption or Reflection); and the effective amplitude of the modulations could be "phased on" to any degree within the design limits, for the calculated solution of thousands of Weather problems. During idling type Weather situations, a sufficient area of the raster was always phased to the Adsorption mode in order to capture either Solar or terrestrial radiant energy in an amount adequate to meet the electrical power demand of the Station.

We can never disregard, nor ever allow to escape our attention, the fact of the immensity of natural Sunlight energy in relation to the cupful that man's technology will ever utilize. Nothing emphasizes this relationship more than the "surface-scratching," but still prodigious achievement of Rayform 27. Even at full-on phasing, R-27's Adsorption-filter pattern in the W/C umbrella can capture only 10% of the Solar input energy. It could never be expected to handle the vast total amount of natural energy brought in via Sunlight. But its 10% capability, the control and redistribution of 45,000,000 Kw at Wamsutter—and even today in our modern W/C stations—is a sizeable, if not an incredible feat. The Weather Control Program was founded on the reasonable goals of Moderation of Weather and Improvement of Climate. Rayform 27's moderate 10% effort, applied in an objectively planned and coordinated schedule, has given EM Age Weather Control an ample leverage to achieve these goals.

In another discounting, as if in further acknowledgment of the immensity of Nature, Rayform 27 Technology finds it feasible to transform into D.C. Electricity no more than 1/10th of 1% of the 10% (45,000,000 per W/C site) that it adsorbs from the Sun. Nonetheless, this "mere" 45,000 KW of electric power, corresponding to mid-day rates, was a most welcome by-product and bonanza for the pioneer Weather Control Station. During off-peak operational hours everyday, Wamsutter was able to sell up to 40,000 KW of its by-product.

The maximum power demand at the pioneer W/C site usually came in the late afternoons or evenings when rain-making frontogeneses were programmed. Rayform 17 systems, carrying their nominal water vapor loads, drew half of the station's 20,000 KW demand, while R-27's Adsorption and Reinsertion could account for another 5,000. Station auxiliaries, including service building facilities, rain-trigger condenser charging equipment, and C-M-A components presented a combined demand of 5,000 KW during rain schedules. On-site R-27 to R-10 Transformation met these maximum electrical demands with ease, as long as the Sun's horizon angle (altitude) exceeded fifteen degrees. Station operation during nighttime was also self-supporting—thriving on a steady 5,000 KW captured from terrestrial radiation by close-down and double raster adsorption techniques.

In the span of the 21st century—the first 100 years of development following Wamsutter—many refinements and improvements in W/C programs and in electric power distribution were added to the original technologies. By mid-century, the reliability of Rayform 27 as a provider of electric power was firmly established. This dependable source of everyday electricity, combined with the Rayform 10 Cross-Continent Power Distribution Grid, spelled the end to the efficacious and utilitarian, but technologically clumsy generation of power by nuclear-fueled steam turbines. And the wireless characteristics of the Rayform 10 Grid, in a similar termination, permitted clearing the landscapes of the millions of grotesque high-tension towers and their pendulous connecting catenaries, a riddance that was finally completed in A.D. 2085—possibly, but very appropriately—in celebration of the 100th birthday of the EM Discoveries.

A.D. 2000

APPROVAL AND ACCEPTANCE

The millennial year A.D. 2000 saw America's Pioneer W/C Station go "on stream," and on exhibition to the astonished world. Wamsutter's immediate operational success, visibly and tangibly demonstrated day after day, removed all doubt that man and his newest ally, the EM Rayforms, had achieved the miracle of Weather Control. An excited world—governments, scientists, rank-and-file citizens, people from all the nations—clamored for participation in the new Technology. They now clearly foresaw the verdant bounty that long-term Weather Control, operating from a thousand, ten thousand, and eventually, from one hundred thousand Wamsutters, could bring to the world. And they also saw W/C Technology as the immediate and practical solution to one of Nature's cruelest localized onslaughts—the SMOG Inversion.

LOS ANGELES—MEXICO CITY—LONDON
—THE MILLENNIUM SMOG DISPERSAL STATIONS

Before the end of that historic millennial year, the United Nations EM Science Council had recommended priority construction of W/C sites in Los Angeles, Mexico City, and London. These three dense metropolises, because of their extreme ratios of smog-index days to population, were favored to become the first beneficiaries of Wamsutter's 15 years of technological development. Hundreds of other fresh-air-short cities around the globe also were placed, in qualifying sequence, on the W/C construction schedule; for few urban areas had been spared from the occasional toxic blending of their environmental exhausts with an uncooperative atmosphere.

The Science of Meteorology tells of the multiple natural factors that play a part in creating stagnant air. Non-rising, vertically stable air can originate from the ingressive subsidence of large unit volumes, or "blocks," of heavy air that are, themselves, the constituents of a massive high pressure Weather system. The descending, sinking action of these blocks is self-compressive and releases heat energy that, in turn and within the block, establishes layers of warm air on top of lower cooler air. Such a temperature inversion, stabilizing the air below the warm layer, also can be produced by terrestrial radiation of heat into a receptive sky layer, or by the condensation (fogging) of water vapor out of a low altitude air mass, and by a variety of other spontaneous Natural events. When one or more of these air-stabilizing factors is dominant, particularly over large valleys or geographic basins such as Wamsutter's Red Desert—and when frontal air movement is absent—a prolonged and inverted stratification of the atmosphere becomes a fact of Weather. If man now mixes the smokes and exhausts of his environment into this combination of low-level fogs, indolent medium-level stratus clouds, and coincident natural dust hazes; he comes up—or down, if you please—with a good case of atmospheric indigestion called SMOG.

LOS ANGELES' SPECIAL PROBLEM—and
A FOUR-SQUARE SOLUTION

In the summertime, air-stabilizing and stagnifying elements of the Weather show up in Los Angeles, California, as though they were meeting for an annual Hobo Convention. They come with a determination and in meteorological combinations that guarantee their tenancy of the Los Angeles air space from the Pacific shore to the encircling San Gabriel Mountains, a coastal basin with an average radius of forty miles. The usual and principal delegate to this gathering is a ponderous giant of subsided maritime air, compressed, moist, frequently chilled into sea fog by its eastward advective crossing of the cold California Ocean Current. Oftentimes, as this weighty, lazy air mass spreads itself into the coastal lowlands and inclines, its sea fog will lift to become one or more stratus cloud layers. And sometimes, just to be different and to show off their versatility, other sluggish air-mass squatters, landlubber vagabonds not even related to the maritime delegate—those of a warmer and of a leaner water vapor content invading from the inland north and east—will disguise their possession of the Los Angeles air space by remaining cloudless. But even in this relatively brighter dress that allows diffused sunlight to glare through the trapped haze and smoke particles, these cloudless air masses show little tendency for vertical air movement; for this is the underlying failure of a stable, inverted air mass.

The Weather Control installation at Los Angeles had full technological flexibility to handle any Weather problem. And during the course of the average Weather-Year—even in the usually balmy climate of southern California—every component of the Station saw at least some action in tempering either the occasional aggressive or regressive tantrums of the local atmosphere. But Los Angeles' special claim to fame was its magnificent performance as "The SMOG Killer."

Some 10 million residents of the Los Angeles-San Gabriel basin were the captive audience whenever a SMOG Inversion slipped into their 40-mile wide amphitheater. For years—almost a half century—this vast crowd of humanity was compelled to sit sheepishly, in total submission, during these irritating and depressing atmospheric displays, which might last for weeks at a time. But now, in the new era of EM Technology, two gallant stars of the Los Angeles Weather Control Company had come to their rescue. Rayforms 17 and 27, still very young and untried in most theaters of the world, waited quietly in the wings for their entrance cues. The audience buzzed with excitement, even as an Inversion dared to approach; for it was already well known

—from their previous 15-year stand in Wamsutter—that the two young W/C Rayforms hated SMOG with a real Western vengeance. And when the torpid trespasser—the gigantic subsiding air mass—finally poured over the fences and pitched camp in the L. A. basin, it was time for #17 and #27 to enter with guns blazing.

Rayform 17 led the attack with skillfully placed water-vapor shots into vulnerable zones of the inverted air mass. Co-star Rayform 27 then followed in one-two fashion with heat-energy jabs into the moisture-conditioned zones set up by R-17. The stagnant air mass, hurting from the combination punches, began to stir. Its smoke and haze particles found themselves caught up and carried along in powerful vertical air currents. And as the energy kicks of R-17 and R-27 gradually spread throughout the huge body of subsided air, the SMOG Inversion knew that eviction was imminent.

During extreme subsidence invasions—those backed by deep and widespread high pressure Weather systems—it was often necessary to schedule continuous air-column stimulation. A twice weekly, controlled extension of the vertical stirring into a frontal pattern brought the site a refreshing rainshower—in itself, a most efficient scrubber of SMOG; and a welcome drink, during the late Summer, for the parched surrounding hillsides. Incidentally, Los Angeles Weather Control put an end to the devastating brush fires that every year dared to come down out of the dry hills into the controlled zone. Some success was achieved also in generating shower lines along the inland perimeters of the W/C area, and in displacing them in the direction of fire outbreaks higher up in the San Gabriel foothills. Forestry officials—and, of course, Smokey the Bear—anxiously awaited the day when Weather Control, with its automatic sprinkler system, would post watch over the timberlands of the world.

Los Angeles Weather Control was a giant step forward, not only in bringing the benefits of moderated Weather to population centers but also in developing the technology of multiple station operation. Because of her huge metropolitan spread, Los Angeles required the coordinated services of four adjoining 10-mile × 10-

mile W/C facilities. The included area of the four-sited complex amounted to 400 square miles, centering on 34° North Latitude and 118° - 15′ West Longitude. Several concessions to existing municipal layouts and structures had to be made in order to adapt W/C plant and equipment to the congested area. But these design modifications were accommodated readily by the new EM technologies, and afforded an opportunity to perfect constructional versatilities. Quite a topical accommodation had to be made in the southeast (Los Alamitos) W/C site by locating the C-M-A building and 23-acre water supply pond inside the Los Alamitos Naval Air Station, three miles south and outside of the W/C area. The other three L. A. sites also had many of their station facilities concessionally scattered, but within their own boundaries. All cardinal sectional lines of the four contiguous sites, however, were positively held to their prescribed latitude and longitude coordinates. During a "four-tie" coordination, the southeast-corner Los Alamitos Station served as master controller, projecting a single 20-mile × 20-mile W/C canopy over the city. This wide-area, reduced-performance coverage found successful and economical application during mild Weather conditions and during the normally pleasant Weather of the winter season. Los Angeles, the first of the multiple-tie W/C stations, provided Weather Control managers with valuable experience in coordinated-site operation and was the forerunner of Zonal and Regional Weather Control.

Although a specially dimensioned and singularly designed W/C system could have been adapted to the total meandering Los Angeles area, the United Nations EM Science Council wisely insisted on the basic 100-square mile, cardinally oriented multiple unit-site design. Within three decades, by A.D. 2030, the Council's guidance was to prove itself well taken, when the 10-, 100-, and 1,000-mile W/C networks of EM OMNI System stations became working realities. Meanwhile, the Los Angeles installation more than fulfilled its mission in the area that it enclosed. Envious outlying suburbs, those outside of the "four-square" boundaries, such as Anaheim, Fullerton, Baldwin, North Burbank, Santa Monica, and even Long Beach, south of the W/C umbrellas, had to wait in patience for their rescue from the age old pangs of seasonally inclement Weather, and from the oppressive SMOGS that were indigenous to their Pacific coastal basin.

MEXICO CITY and LONDON—
THE TWIN W/C CITIES

While Los Angeles was struggling for five years, from A.D. 2000 to A.D. 2005, with the installation of her four contiguous W/C sites and their interlocking facilities, Mexico City had its standard 10-mile × 10-mile W/C Station in partial operation after only one year of construction. And by late A.D. 2002 aided and augmented by a Rayform 17 Pacific Water Supply System and a local EM Elemental Separator used in water purification, the pioneer Latin American Station was running a full time SMOG-dispersal and Rainshower schedule.

The totally cooperative, appreciative, and dedicated Mexican people entered into the new EM Technological Age with a confidence and enthusiasm that had yet to find its equal among the unsettled, socially perplexed nations of the world. Mexican builders and technicians, who had emerged in the final decade of the 20th century as world leaders in both the architectural and mechanical fields, achieved a lasting quality along with remarkable quantitative progress in their W/C construction. The southeast corner Main Control Center, C-M-A building, and Water Supply Park in the suburb of Ixtapalapa was so classically and durably built that it is, still today, an architectural "garden spot" of the country. Ixtapalapa Park ranks with the pyramids of Teotihuacán as one of Mexico's, and the world's, most impressive monuments commemorating a cultural age of man.

Halfway around the world across the Atlantic Ocean and 33 degrees north of Mexico City's latitude, an identical standard Weather Control was concurrently (A.D. 2001 to A.D. 2005) installed at London, England. These two great cities, London and Mexico, presented almost identical surface outlines to their W/C umbrellas. Except for a few radial suburbs, both cities contained themselves completely within the 100 square miles of their standard 10 × 10 sites. London's amazing density of 8,000,000 inhabitants inside the controlled area was closely matched by the teeming population of Mexico's capital city. There was no question that both of these concentrations of human life needed the air-freshening and SMOG-dispersal that EM Weather Control could bring.

While their demographic densities bore a striking similarity, the origins of, and even the day-to-day Weather of the two metropolises could hardly be more different. London, at sea level, frequently was compelled to bathe herself in the fogs and stratus overcasts that brewed under the pervasive influence of the warm North Atlantic Current. And Mexico City, high up at 7,400 feet elevation at the head of the great Valley of Mexico, breathes an atmosphere that for six months of the year scarcely shows trace of ever having passed over an ocean. The piked rims of the Valley —the encircling Sierra Madre Mountain Ranges to the east, west, and south—extract almost all of the water vapor from maritime air masses that dare to ascend inland from the Gulf of Mexico or from the vast Pacific. Stable, continentally heated and reheated air, locked within the Valley of Mexico, becomes a ready trap for haze and smoke.

Weather Control techniques pay little mind to the varied origins of air stagnation and SMOG. The existence of a Weather condition, per se, establishes the problem; and solutions are computed to suit the character and attributes of each local air mass condition. It was of interest—and it certainly did not pass unnoticed by the millions of EM Technology watchers around the world—that similar Rayform 17-27 W/C techniques were utilized at Los Angeles, London, and Mexico City despite differences in the origins and in the particular specifications of their Weather problems. Weather Control Technology had demonstrated in the three "Millennium Stations" that it could handle the full range of Nature's atmospheric tantrums.

Public approval of a new technology is sometimes indicated by the popular appellation or nickname that becomes attached to the subject. Los Angeles, as noted, called its system: The SMOG Killer. Londoners appreciatively labeled their W/C unit: The Blue Sky Maker. And Mexicanos, never known to be lacking in their words of praise, embellished Mexico City's Weather Control as:

*El Brazo Derecho de Nuestra Senora de Ixtapalapa Que Barre
El Polvo del Cielo*—"The Strong Right Arm of our Lady of
Ixtapalapa That Sweeps the Dirt from the Sky."

WEATHER CONTROL EXPANDS INTO THE 21st
CENTURY
WORLDWIDE COVERAGE: A PART OF THE OMNI
SYSTEM

The 21st century was the construction era of the EM Age.
There has never been, in the recorded history of modern man, a
century of time so productive, so expansionary, and so inclusive
of all nations in a common effort. The worldwide advancement
of the EM Technologies inspired and fostered the broadest cultural revolution, one that was not limited to the Sciences, but
equally manifest in the Nationalistic, Humanistic, and even the
Theological attitudes of all men and nations. It is noteworthy that
the bold concept of worldwide Weather and Climate Control set
the pace and established the constructional pattern of technological progress—and at the same time may have been, in itself,
more than just a silent witness to this emergence of a new harmony among and between all peoples.

Each new Weather Control site that went "on stream," following Wamsutter and the three Millennium Stations, was its own
best salesman. The day-to-day achievement of controlled Weather,
and the growing evidence of climatic and land quality improvement at the new sites were the talk of the world. Every nation
around the globe had enjoined itself into the excitement of EM
Science and was participating in the manufacture of components
for EM technological projects. By A.D. 2030 more than 1,000
industrial complexes in 50 different lands were turning out C-M-A's
(Converter-Magnetizer-Accelerators) at an annual production
rate of 100,000 units, half of which went into Weather Control
service. The other 50,000 units per year, many of them portable
and aerospace mobile in design, found assignment in P.M.I. Propulsion and in Elemental Separation categories. The C-M-A, of
course, is the basic building block in all of the EM Technologies,

for it is in the C-M-A that the "unearthly" or non-naturally existing Rayforms—such as Rayforms 17 and 27 of Weather Control
—are constituted and reconstituted for their 10 seconds of useful
service life.

By mid-century, every urban area of the Earth with a population of 10,000 or more had its own 10 × 10 Local Weather
Control Station. These municipal sites, impartially and judiciously
placed in the construction schedule by the United Nations EM
Science Council, served to bring the benefits of the W/C program
in priority to the most people. Every one of the thousands of
scattered urban W/C sites, however, was installed on exact latitude
and longitude coordinates consistent with its ultimate placement
and mission in the worldwide W/C pattern. The long-range goal
for EM Technology, so zealously promoted and defended by the
Science Council, called for the incorporation of many of the new
technologies and their services into the OMNI System. It was important, therefore, that Weather Control construction be considerate and cognizant of its subordinate role within the OMNI.
The fact that the OMNI System today shares the same performing
stage—the 10-, 100-, and 1,000-mile squared networks around
the globe—that originally was designed for Weather Control, is
undoubtedly a commendation to the importance and technological
value placed on the subject Wonder.

While the cities of the world were building their Weather Control umbrellas, a parallel construction of W/C sites in the open
country, across the prairies, the deserts, and the mountains of all
seven continents had been going well. Mid-century saw achievement of the 25% completion mark in the worldwide construction
goal of 400,000 land-site W/C stations. And, of the additional
250,000 maritime W/C sites planned, 10,000 were already operational; these principally located along the ocean shorelines, and
having standard land-based station facilities. In North America
and Europe, 10-mile × 10-mile cross-continental continuous W/C
stripes on every integral parallel of latitude had been completed.
At each 100 and 1,000 mile East-West interval along these continuous stripes, Zonal (100 × 100 mile) and Regional (1,000 ×
1,000 mile) North-South net-tie provisions were incorporated. It

was possible, even in this early stage of coordinated control, in A.D. 2050, to monitor up to a million square miles as one W/C Region. The United States, for example, could be Weather-Coordinated under as few as three Regional W/C umbrellas; and Weather solutions for all three could be programmed simultaneously from the North American Continental Control Center, MKC, at Kansas City, Missouri.

Each successive year in this amazing EM Construction Era was witness to an increasing rate of return from the enormous investment—an investment measured not only in financial and material wealth but in terms of lifetimes of human effort and application. As more and more Local 10 × 10 unit blocks in the continental W/C systems fell into place, gradually tieing the great nets together, the benefits of coordinated multiple-station Weather solutions became a reality. The tremendous latent energies of State-sized, or even million square mile-sized air masses came under the combined scrutiny and analysis of the total system. One thousand or ten thousand unit W/C sites could be teamed to meet the encroachment of a large Weather system. From this time on, it was clearly a contest between systems; the great Natural System of the Atmosphere versus the infinitely weaker but highly levered Technology of large System Weather Control.

THE BEAUTY OF SYSTEM WEATHER CONTROL

"Early Warning" or the long-range observation and calculus of Weather inclinations is the paramount added capability of System Weather Control. Early Warning enables a distant anticipation of tempest, drought, or of any of the other violent Natural solutions to the atmosphere's continuous thermodynamic adjustment, and it prescribes the relatively mild preventive medicine while the potential Weather upset is in the formative stages. Under the thousands of probes and sensors in System Weather Control, the state of Weather in a Zone or Region becomes a computerized expression, a numerical input, representing a summation of the integrals (themselves summations) of all the inter-related physical attributes that describe an air mass. Since Weather is a manifestation and an expression of one of the forms of Nature's energy, the computer input—in its special language—is also a statement of energy. It is a statement of the sensible dynamic components— the wind force and the momentum of the air mass—and of their impellers, the latent energies hidden within the atmosphere's contiguous water vapors. And it includes factors representing the several other contributors to the problem: Solar input energy, terrestrial radiation, and pressure and temperature gradients arising from proximate air masses. Indeed, the summed expression of a Weather condition is a complex number, but one that is right at home within the Computer-Comparators that solve the Weather Energy-Balance Equation.

The beauty—at least another advantage—of System Weather Control is that it can put a "number" on any sized Weather block; and in corresponding fashion, can set up its Computer-Comparators to solve the Equation for any sized area. System Weather Control, which became an increasingly applied W/C technique during the last half of the 21st century, offered W/C managers the versatility to summarize Weather attributes and inclinations over a range from one unit volume to 10,000 unit volumes. Specifically, a "number" could be put on any 1,000 cubic mile unit volume above a typical 10 × 10 Local Station, or on the Zonal volume representing up to 100 stations; or when its suited a regional-area Weather circumstance, a summation number could be hung onto the huge air volume above a 1,000-mile Regional square equal to ⅓ the area of the U.S.A.

System Weather Control brought about a new definition and concept of EM Technology. No longer was W/C a specialized instrument serving only a particular area and its local inhabitants. It was now part of a larger, all inclusive order. It was Weather Control characteristic of the EM OMNI System. The world was beginning to grasp an appreciation of this expanded concept, for with the completion of each new link in the W/C pattern the way was paved for related technologies to join the OMNI. Cross-continent W/C stripes on the latitude parallels, completed in North America and in Europe by mid-century, turned their East-West coordinates—the latitude parallels—into 2,000-mile-long,

straight-shot pipelines for not only W/C data but also for Rayform #10 Electric Power, Rayform 17 Pumped Water Vapor,
and a host of other Rayform burdens in the transportation and
communication media. Although it was still a generation away to
its "first completion," the OMNI was already the focus of world
attention. (Indeed, the worldwide EM OMNI may never reach
a state of "final completion," in the sense that even in our time it
is constantly taking on new assignments and undergoing continual
equipment updating, in its responsibility as administrator, coordinator, and distributor of all the Wonders of EM Technology.)

In A.D. 2080, after an 80-year construction period, the Weather
Control installation goals of the EM Science Council had been
reached. A worldwide total of 650,000 W/C station sites were in
operation. Continental stations accounted for 400,000; and coastal
and off-shore facilities that covered the maritime areas of the
globe in a lesser concentration, totaled a quarter million units.
Nowhere on the surface of the Earth was there a square mile
that did not feel the effects of modified, controlled Weather. Some
of the mid-ocean and deep Polar areas, of course, did not warrant
the same investment as the population and population-support
zones; but even these remote areas came under the cover of 100
× 100-mile Zonal-area Weather Control.

In the remaining 20 years of this fabulous Century of EM
Construction, another interesting, though not unexpected change
in popular assessment came to Weather Control Technology. Because of their far-reaching economic influence, the worldwide Climatic Improvements wrought by 50 years of System Weather
Control became more famous and prominent than the technological means that begat and evolved them. This switch in public
interest from the techniques of W/C to its product, Climate Improvement, has persisted over the interim 900 years even into our
own time. There are many citizen-technicians today, who, in a
state of blissful accustomation, know nothing of the mechanics
of the amazing Weather Control umbrellas. W/C canopies are
there, it seems, like the Sun that rises and sets every day, and are
only indirectly acknowledged, in deference to more pressing interests that command the attention of modern EM man. Perhaps

it is because Weather Control has become so familiar to us, like
the air that surrounds us, that we do not see it or place it in a
position of acclaim. But in the final analysis, it is right that we
do not lose ourselves in the invention, but rather, in its purpose
and utility. As we shift our sights, then, from short-term Weather
Control to long-range Climate Improvement, we join with the
EM world of A.D. 2100 to acknowledge youthful Weather Control's transition into its prime majority. That this recognition of
the bountiful effects of Weather Control Technology came so
rapidly and positively, during the very first century of our Age,
attests to Climate Improvement's prominent role in our EM
environment.

THE CLIMATE IMPROVEMENT
and LAND RECLAMATION PROGRAM

The rise and reign of Climate Improvement is best told in
combination with the story of its own private contractor, the Land
Reclamation Program. And, of course, the stage that they both
share and that brings life and substance to both, is the worldwide
consolidation of all the EM technological services, the EM OMNI.

BUT FIRST—for background, again—A QUICK LOOK AT A
FEW MILLION YEARS OF TIME
——AND SOME PRE-CAMBRIAN, PLIOCENE,
AND PLEISTOCENE PROBLEMS

Who among us would not readily agree that our Earth is
blessed with a unique and most propitious distribution of land
and sea; one that has permitted man, by geographic and climatic
circumstances more than by his own wits, to emerge from the
crude state of his ancient creation. (Or, if your personal philosophy has bought you a ticket as a transcendentalist voyager, we
can restate the premise to acknowledge that the land-sea propor-
tionment in the recent 10 million years has certainly favored man's
past, present, and ever-continuing transcension.) Earth's one-
quarter land, three-quarters sea topographical plan, with its oceanic

North Polar radiator and vast continental South Polar heat exchanger, and subject to the tremendous power of the Sun, has
become by fortuitous combination, a place for man.

But in the 6,000 million years since its nebulous origin in
mysterious Pre-Cambrian time, Planet Earth has pitched, flipped,
and wobbled countless times, fighting to hold position within the
spinning configuration of the celestial galaxy. During this incomprehensible measure of time, each of Earth's aberrations from its
usual ephemerisical conservatism has shaken its continents and
oceans loose from their anchors, and subjected them to dramatic
changes in shape, texture, and climate. Flat, hot deserts in one
period of geological time have become frozen oceans in another.
Mountains have risen and fallen, and who knows how many
times and with what violence the geological tops-to-bottoms have
inter-changed themselves.

Somewhere and somehow, in this perpetuity of time, man
entered the picture. He obviously waited until the majority of the
shaking had abated, since we have no record of his footprints
prior to the most recent 1,000,000 years. Perhaps Pleistocene
Stone Age man did have predecessors—it seems a waste to have
had the Earth empty of his "talents" for the previous 5,999 million years—but the vastness of time makes even this conjecture a
futile line of thought, serving no purpose. We do know, however,
that modern man, the physical beast that he is today, contoured
himself and shaped up—in a length of arms and ovality of cranium
aspect—only 11,000 years ago. So it is in this miniscule of time,
the past 11,000 years. that our view of the Earth's fortunate
topographic proportions becomes relevant to the history of human adaptation and emergence.

From a structural-geology standpoint, the Earth has been
behaving itself during these latest 11,000 years, except for a
minor earthquaking stress adjustment here and there. In fact,
the surface structure of Earth has not really changed noticeably
since early Pliocene Period, some 10,000,000 years ago. The same
quiet status quo, however, cannot be claimed by its Climates; for
they have been going through continuous modifications imposed
by the relentless grinding mill of the Great Ice Age Cycles, the

youngest of which is still actively working on us. Since the pre-sumed first "cold snap" in early Pliocene time, when the Antarctic ice cap started to form, icing-melting cycles have followed an average calendar of 50,000 years. Some have taken as long as 80,000 years to make the round trip from cold to warm and back to cold again. But in the more recent 1,000,000 years associated with Stone Age man, there have been some "short" cycles of only 20,000 years.

Our present point in time appears to be about 11,000 years into one of these 20,000-year cycles that began in 8000 B.C. with a warming trend. Quite possibly, Noah's biblical lifesaving voyage was occasioned by the glacial thaw and flood that marked this warm beginning of our present division of geological time—the Holocene Period. At any rate, modern man's Ice Age Cycle is a moderate one—as Ice Age Cycles go—both in duration and in the amplitude of its warming and cooling swings. Its melting labors in the 8th century B.C. are termed "partial," in that they only fractionally dented the ponderous Antarctic ice cap. 7,000,000 cubic *miles* of ice remain there today, much of it over two miles thick, out of an estimated cold-peak balance, eons ago, of some 9,000,000 cubic miles. The vastness of Antarctica is often over-looked. With its 5½ million square miles the South Polar Con-tinent is approximately twice the size of Australia, and even 1½ times the area of Europe. Moreover, it is a tremendous storehouse of frozen water, capable of raising the Earth's ocean level by 250 feet, if and when it melts again.

In the Northern Hemisphere, the 8th-century B.C. warming trend cut a little more ice—as they say—and was successful in melting 6,000,000 cubic miles of glacial burden. (A cool 1,000,000 still remain on Greenland.) Thus, the total melt in the opening days of Holocene time was sufficient to raise the level of the seas 330 feet, at which mark it remained constant for 10,000 years until A.D. 2100, the transfer date into the cold half-cycle of our present Ice Age. At this "cold" awakening 900 years ago, the United Nations EM Science Council, then with only a raw 100 years experience behind it in System Weather and Climate Con-trol, made some giant-sized decisions—that most favorably affect us today and will preserve future generations from "shoveling snow in the tropics."

Sea levels in A.D. 2100 had already dropped 6 feet, as the ocean waters began to reposition themselves into deepening glaciers around the Poles. Predictions for A.D. 3000, 10% into the current Ice Age Cold Cycle, showed that by that year the 50% point in the ebb of Noah's flood (the 330-foot rise of 8000 B.C.) would have been reached; and the complete ebb was scheduled by A.D. 3500. During all of this chilling phase a super dense, impenetrable cloud cover, spawned in both Polar regions, would have increasingly slugged itself down over three-quarters of the Earth, progressively feeding its own perpetuation and denying the world any rescue, in spite of the sunshine's willing, but locked-out warmth. Facing these formidable prospects, the U.N. Science Council in A.D. 2100, decided to do battle, using the facilities of EM science and technology to thwart Nature's unreined deliverance of Earth into another glacial oblivion.

THE THREE GOALS OF CLIMATE IMPROVEMENT

EM Weather and Climate Control, on the grand system approach afforded by the world-wide OMNI disposition, had three principal long-range goals. These goals were established 900 years ago, in A.D. 2100, and have persisted into our era as the guiding fundamentals of the program. They are as follows:

● First, Prevention of the Ice Age takeover.

● Second, Climatic Improvement of the presently inhabited and potentially habitable areas of the Earth.

● Third, Reclamation and Reconstitution of the Earth's desert areas (totaling 10,000,000 square miles) and of the semi-arid wastelands (20,000,000 square miles)—a face-lifting project of huge proportion encompassing more than half of the land surface of the globe.

The day by day W/C techniques employed in the Climate Improvement program are similar for all three of the long range aims. A passing observer would be unable to tell which goal was under attack. The geographic point of application, together with the degree and persistence of each W/C technique, are the effective variables of Climate Improvement Technology as it pursues a combined resolution of the three goals.

PREVENTION OF THE ICE AGE TAKEOVER

It is somewhat paradoxical that we little realize we are living within a tremendous, constantly progressing Ice Age. Obviously, this is because our personal measure of lifetime is so insignificant in relation to the Ice Age Cycle, or even to the half-cycle that is now taking the world to a cold peak in A.D. 7000. It is altogether probable that Stone Age man, surrounded by thousand foot thick glaciers, similarly did not realize that a Cycle was in progress; so accustomed was he and hundreds of his prior generations to the "same old thing." The pervasive folds of the environment had become so much a part of him, as they are with us too, that he could not fathom the possibility of any other type of surrounding.

With commendable prudence the U.N. EM Science Council, in A.D. 2100, reaffirmed that Nature should never be entirely subdued. Even with the power of EM Technology now at their call to effect a 100% reversal of many Natural trends, including the total prevention of the oncoming Ice Cap, the Science Council wisely elected to allow the Ice Age Cycle to live—but, as we know, under a heavy restraint. There is always present in Nature the chance of collision-course combinations that can wreak a havoc far worse than the relative discomforts of our normal, though imposed, environment. And there is a certain degree of geo-physical ballast and stability in the established Natural cycles. In this understanding, the Council committed itself and the planet to a program that would reduce the Ice Age's cold ebb by 80%, allowing it to run to only 20% of its predicted Natural extreme. In place of the 330-foot sea level drop by A.D. 3500 with its corresponding transplant of 8,000,000 cubic miles of ice onto the Polar caps, the cold ebb will be limited to an ultimate 66 feet of ocean drop and 1,600,000 additional unit "blocks" (cubic miles) of Polar ice. Still, in our day or in any 100 generations, the world will hardly notice the workings of the 20% Modified Ice Age

Cycle; because the ocean drop has been adjusted to a mere 12 feet per millennium, and full ebb will be held off until A.D. 7000.

A look at the energy equivalents represented in all this ice gives us another clue to the size of things and suggests why we cannot always comprehend the dimensions of Nature. If the Ice Age were to run its normal course, and return some 8 to 10 million cubic miles of ice to the Polar Caps in the 1,500 years ending in A.D. 3500, the heat-energy removal required to fill this order would amount to 2×10^{20} B.T.U.s per *year*. Yet, the gross *daily* input of the Sun onto the Earth exceeds this annual amount of ice-making energy by 300 million times. Obviously then, the formation of Polar Ice Caps depends on the "circumstance" of a major percentage of the Earth's surface being shielded from Sunshine, while at the same time, the growing Ice Caps wildly radiate the declining balance of terrestrial heat through the thin atmospheric blankets that cover the Poles. No doubt, once a glacial cycle gets a hold, the dense clouds that would inundate most of the Earth (except in the Polar regions) will contribute at an exponential rate to the progression of the freeze—as will also the changing topographical features, such as the shallowing ice-choked Arctic Ocean outlet at the Bering Straights. Weather Control techniques in the Ice Age Prevention effort, therefore, focus on the average cloud-cover trends measured over the entire middle and upper latitude belts of the Earth; never permitting a self-feeding, multiplying type build-up of cloud cover to take over control of the world's Climates.

WHY BOTHER?

If we will hardly notice the effects of the Modified Ice Age, you may ask, why pay all this investigative tribute to it? Here are a couple of answers to this reasonable question:

First—Look where we would be if EM Technology had not reduced the Ice Age ebb to only 66 feet. The world's gain in coastal acreage from the additional exposure of the ocean's continental shelves would be small recompense for the glacial walls that again would have buried Europe, North America, and Siberia.

And as a second answer, if you are interested in Natural Physical Theories, consider this extract from the archives of the Joint U.S.A.-U.S.S.R. Natural Geophysical Society, Vol. 17, p. 27, dated February, A.D. 1999:

"Although even today there is not a unanimous agreement in the EM Science Council, the Precession Theory of Planetary Axis Change (PITPAC) has been of concern to geophysical scientists for many centuries. This theory proposes that, in the eons ago, topographic unbalance, resulting from polar ice-mass accumulations, could have been the physical cause of the cataclysmic readjustments in the orientation of the Earth's north-south axis.

"Like a spinning top—the theory holds—the Earth's state of equilibrium on its inertial plane depends on constant mass distribution; particularly on its surface, where increments of mass most strongly influence its revolving dynamic balance. The great ocean ebbs and the corresponding Polar Cap accumulations during past glacial cycles have involved significant and measureable fractions of the Earth's total mass. The transposition of these huge amounts from the oceans—which predominate Southern Hemisphere topography—to positions of incredible height and thickness on the Polar Caps—and particularly onto the Northern Hemisphere Pole—could have provoked Global Precession—according to the PITPAC Theory.

In place of another repetition of this physically possible holocaust, our only material concern and reminder of what could have restaged it, is the 300 cubic miles of new ice (or excess water) that the oceans must give up each year to keep in balance with the 20% Modified Ice Age Cycle. (300 cubic miles is the annual volume derived from the 5,000-year spread of 1,600,000 cubic miles of ice corresponding to the ultimate sea level drop of 66 feet.) But the composite plan for world Climate and Land Improvement has received the annual bonanza of 300 cubic miles of new water with open arms. This new supply, equal to approximately three Lake Eries (one of North America's five Great Lakes) per year, has been at a most useful and timely rate. And there has been no need, so far, to waste any of it in portentous storage in the polar ice boxes.

CLIMATE IMPROVEMENT'S FAVORITE SPORT: LEAP FROG

Basic cloud cover and 10% sunlight control within Local and Zonal W/C sites will probably always be the principal heat regulating techniques in Climate Improvement. But aside from these mainstays, there have been several technological innovations that have become valuable contributors, particularly in the fields of heat redistribution and apportionment. One that adds measurably to the over-all success of the Climate Improvement Program has been "Leap Frog."

Project Leap Frog became a powerful tool of Weather and Climate Control Technology at the turn into the 22nd century. Operating on the world-circling OMNI's 10 × 10 and 100 × 100 networks, Leap Frog is a technique using Rayform 27's amazing infrared adsorption capability—adapted to a latitude-jumping "game" of Solar Energy Transposition. This EM W/C branch technology has the faculty to take consignment of 5% of the infrared Sunshine energy at a tropical location, then to ship it, boxed as a Rayform 27 burden, in a series of giant arches up and over 10 degrees of latitude. From any landing, the consignment can again be projected northward (southward in the Southern Hemisphere) to a final point of destination where its tropical heat load is added directly to the Sun's local effort.

Essentially, Leap Frog joins with the Atmosphere and Ocean Currents in the transportation of heat energy from equatorial and tropical zones toward the Poles. For Planet Earth to maintain its average annual temperature, it is necessary that the heat received from the Sun be offset by heat radiated back out to space—our old friend, the Heat Balance Equation. And the global shape of Earth, of course, is the geometry that makes its solution a gigantic and complex heat-flow problem.

Leap Frog's transfer of Solar heat northward and southward from the Equator is usually scheduled to moderate the cool sea-

sonal Climate in the receiving zone. However, the translocation
of even 5% of a block of Solar Energy has the dual effect of lowering temperatures in the tropics, as well as raising them in the
colder latitudes. With its heat input rate of 20,000,000 KW (7 ×
10^{10}B.T.U./Hour) per 100 square mile Standard W/C area,
Leap Frog has been able to combine with Natural Solar impingement in many temperate and sub-Polar regions to effectively make
winter a 2-month season.

THE BUILDING BLOCKS:
HEAT—WATER—MINERAL

The EM Science Council's three goals for Climate Improvement recognized that an agreeable Climate, in itself, was quite
useless unless there were a productive piece of real estate under
it. With both Climate and real estate in mind, it might be said
that the three goals, reduced to a material accounting, propose
an adequate total supply and an effective apportionment of each
of Nature's three building blocks: Heat, Water, and Minerals.

Nature's haphazard distribution of Solar Heat—as we have
seen—goes through the reapportionment mill of Weather and
Climate Control and comes out more synergetic with man's use
of the topography. Water, as the object of Regional Rainfall Equa-
lization, feels the confining leash of W/C Technology. But the
tremendous total quantities of Water, in addition to rainfall, involved in satisfying all three of the long-range goals of Climate
Improvement are beyond the logistic capacity of the Rayform 17
facilities in Weather Control. In fact, Water is the common denominator in the resolution of each of the goals and is, by far, the
largest volume of material handled by the EM Technologies. The
task of relocating all this Water—and a considerable side order
of soil Mineral—in the construction of that better piece of real
estate falls to the province of the Land Reclamation Program.

A 30,000,000 SQUARE MILE GARDEN PROJECT

The earth has 57½ million square miles of land area. Some
10 million of this forever will be hopeless for general habitation.

In this category are the major portions of Antarctica, Greenland, other Arctic fringes; and even many vast tracts of mountainous rockland on all the continents, which offer man only a special use and a limited opportunity for survival. The Land Reclamation Program has not concentrated nor expended much time and material transport on these unpromising regions. (Yet we live in an age of technological miracles, and who can predict the future of these present voids?) Economic practicability has centered Land Reclamation activity in other, more yielding areas of the world.

In A.D. 2100, when System Weather Control was just beginning to show its beneficial effects, a master plan was established to reconstitute and improve more than half of the Earth's surface area, so that future generations would be able to utilize the full bounty of EM Weather and Climate Improvement. At that time, more than ten million square miles of the Earth were absolute desert country—receiving less than 10 inches of sporadic rainfall annually and where the evaporation rate far exceeded the moisture input. Surrounding the desert areas there additionally were some 20,000,000 square miles of semi-arid land, ranging from unprofitable tillage to barren wasteland. This combined 30,000,000 square mile larger half of the Earth's total land mass owed its pauperous state to a universal lack of soil moisture. The uselessness of this vast domain was compounded—in many regions—by its textural inadequacy and a general deficiency in the supportive soil Minerals. The EM Science Council knew that if the moisture and mineral balances in these soils could be restored to an agricultural quality, maintenance of the new land in its rejuvenated condition could then be guaranteed by EM Weather and Climate Control Technology. Life-sustaining rainfall and a regulated cloud-cover protection from the burning Sunshine were waiting an opportunity to service this long-lost half of the Earth's terrain.

The face lifting of the abandoned half into an agricultural cornucopia was indeed an extravagant, preposterous challenge; but, in the dawn of EM time, there was logic and timeliness to this proposition. Land Reclamation on the grand scale would consume the mountains of reconstituted bulk and gangue-type by-products of the new Age, particularly those generated by EM Elemental Separation Technology. Land Reclamation also would fill a most necessary role as receiving agent for the compulsory annual supply of new Water originating from the Science Council's Ice Age Prevention Program. And the 30,000,000 square miles of fertile, life-supportive new land, nourished by these unlimited resources of Minerals and Water, would become home, farmstead, vacation site, and healthful country living for the millions of people who had found themselves trapped inside the concrete jungles of the world.

H_2O N P K
WATER NITROGEN PHOSPHORUS POTASSIUM

The Land Reclamation master plan called for the reconstitution of the soils in the desert and semi-arid lands under its jurisdiction. Reconstitution was to be achieved by a Water and Mineral relocation program that would necessarily continue for centuries—indeed, it is still in progress today. Desert areas were scheduled to receive 36 inches of maintained, permanent "soil-water," this to be blended with imported soil Minerals to form an ideal sandy loam. Semi-arid areas would get an additional 24 inches of permanent Water, to texturize their soils into equally ideal conditions. The total volume of Water involved in reconstituting these 30,000,000 square miles is close to 12,000 cubic miles. (How large—or small—a drink this is, we shall see later.) And Mineral matter necessary to bring the arid half of Earth's topography up to agricultural quality has amounted to the greatest fertilizer job in history! Each acre in the 30,000,000 square-mile project will eventually—by completion date in A.D. 3100—receive 15 tons of reconstituting Minerals. The average per acre blend consists of 6 tons of Potash (K_2O) equivalent, 4 tons each of Phosphoric Oxides (P_2O_5) and soluble Nitrates (NO_3), and a ton of mixed secondary and micro-nutrients. U.N. Agronomy Council experts keep a close watch on the special formula-blend needed for each zone undergoing reclamation. At the present time, after close to 900 years in the Land Reclamation Program, the original goals are within sight and should be fulfilled within the next 100 years.

THE EARTH MOVERS
PUMPS AND BARGES

At Land Reclamation's inception in the 21st century, its conservative managers aimed at a production pace of 30,000 square miles annually; predicated upon the availability of Mineral resources from the Elemental Separation Plants of the global OMNI System, and from the thousands of large-scale Coastal and Cross-River Elemental Separation stations around the world. In the beginning there were colossal problems associated with the transportation of Water and Minerals to the reclamation zones. But during the mid-century period, a dedicated industrial and manufacturing effort eased the logistic strain by producing the remarkable BGPM (Billion Gallon Per Minute) Rayform 17 Water Delivery facilities, and the LANDREC Fleet of 5,000 P.M.I.-Propelled 1,000-ton freighters. These two material handling giants —BGPM for Water, and LANDREC for Mineral cargo—so familiar to travelers around the globe, are, in themselves, almost a Wonder of the Age.

The BGPM Water Delivery System consists of 1,000 Rayform 17 long-range pumping stations located over the face of the globe and taking suction from all the oceans. Each station has the voracious capacity of 1,200,000 gallons per minute—one hundred times greater than the original Pacific System pumps used to supply Wamsutter and other Local W/C sites. To match every pumping station there is a downstream receiver station that "catches" and unloads the Rayform 17 carriers and then completes the local short-haul delivery. Receiver stations are often located as distant as 10,000 trajectorial miles from their ocean pumps; and being "portable" in design, are periodically relocated to follow the working face and the particular demands of the Land Reclamation Program. Yet, even with their tremendous unit capacity, the 1,000 pumps and receivers of BGPM must operate at better than 80% efficiency for 24 hours daily and every day of the year, to move their total annual cargo of 300 cubic miles of Water. (Can you imagine what a job the Atmosphere has done in pumping the 7,000,000 cubic miles of Water onto Antarctica—or even the 1,000,000 cubic miles of water onto Greenland).

Mineral relocation, at the 15-ton-per-acre rate required to put an agricultural capability into the "other" half of the Earth's soils, became the Herculean task—and the proving ground—for the P.M.I. 1,000-ton LANDREC Standard freighter. These modular, low-altitude vessels are equipped with minimal 1.01 GeeForce engines, which, though strong and able, are not highly torqued for rapid departures. Identical bow and stern structural lines of the Standard freighters do not attempt to disguise their efficient square shapes or to hide their functional bottom-loading maws. LANDREC Standard freighters have beams of 20 feet, equal to their depths, and have overall lengths of just 60 feet. As a rule, during a voyage, groups of 50 vessels are magnetically clamped into a compact 600-foot-by-100-foot barge formation; and thus have a combined 50,000-ton unit barge capacity. Based on anticipated annual loading rates of 300 million tons derived from Elemental Separation Sources, the specially assigned LANDREC Fleet of 5,000 Mineral haulers continues to make at least 60 round trips yearly between cargo source sites and Land Reclamation zones.

Most of the effort of the minimal 1.01 GeeForce engines in LANDREC freighters is expended in counter-gravity support; but it is not unusual for barge formations on long hauls to cruise at 100 miles per hour, a velocity that they readily attain in 10 minutes of acceleration. Very rarely do the barge formations, or even singly dispatched freighters, fly above 1,000-foot elevation; although, like all P.M.I. vessels, there is no limitation to their trajectory—other than "common sensibility." During the second and third centuries of fleet operation, from A.D. 2250 to A.D. 2450, with an increased availability of Elemental Separation products, the LANDREC Fleet was able to double up on schedule, delivering Minerals to 60,000 square miles in each of those many years. Since then, however, economic balance favors the original 30,000 square mile annual Reclamation goal, and this is the Mineral transportation rate still maintained today.

ONE THOUSAND LAKES—in three sizes—
STANDARD, DOUBLE STANDARD,
AND TRIPLE STANDARD

It has been remarkable how the several EM Technologies, both the product generators and the product receivers in the Land Reclamation Program, have coordinated and cooperated in the utilization of materials. The one exception, of course, has been the yearly supply of 300 cubic miles of Ice Age Water. This constant, compulsory volume of incoming Water is far in excess of Land Reclamation's soil-water demands, which amount to a mere 12 to 15 cubic miles per year, or only 5% of the 300 cubic mile annual "gift." By the year A.D. 3000, 270,000 cubic miles of sea Water will have to be relocated inland to satisfy the Ice Age Prevention commitment. Arithmetically, and obviously, there has to be a much more thirsty customer out there than the 15 cubic-mile-per-year soil re-moisturizing program.

Since the 21st century, Land Reclamation managers have used every ingenuity to receive and distribute the relentless influx of Ice Age Water. Their one greatest aid in this enormous globe-circling diversion of Water has been the One Thousand Lakes Project. One Thousand Lakes, like the LANDREC Fleet and the BGPM System, is another sub-project within the Land Reclamation Program. No smalltime drinker, the Lakes Project easily can handle twenty times the volume that goes into soil-water re-moisturization. With a receiving capacity designed to keep pace with the mammoth BGPM Water Delivery System, One Thousand Lakes becomes a voracious and insatiable consumer of any or all of the annual 300 cubic miles.

The 1,000 man-made lakes, all of which are now geographically established—except that the final 100 are still filling—have been located strategically around the world and have played an important role in the stabilization of continental Weather. Lakes come in three sizes: Standard, Double Standard, and Triple Standard—to meet most any geographical surface outline and vertical accommodation. Standard-sized lakes contain 100 cubic miles of Water and resemble North America's Lake Erie in volume, though not necessarily in area or depth. The existing 1,000 lakes of the project are about equally allocated to the three Standard sizes. Several have great depths of more than 3,000 feet; and at least 50 lakes have what lakeologists call "open bottoms." These—so far—have been a great asset to the overall program, because they require continual filling; their Waters forever seeping and sinking into the vast and mysterious underground reservoirs within the Earth—from whence, perhaps, all Waters originally emanated.

Mixed rows of connected Standard lakes have been spotted along the leeward sides of the great mountain ranges on all the continents and are very effective in an advective restoration of moisture into these dehydrated "mountain shadow" air masses. There are hundreds of Standard lakes deep within the former desert lands of the world. The boundless Sahara and Gobi regions alone have some 300 Double and Triple Standard lakes, whose surfaces aid in keeping local air masses charged with the water vapor needed for forming protective cloud covers and refreshing rain showers.

AN INSPECTION TRIP AROUND
THE WORLD FEDERATION

Many times it is the by-product that reaps the applause while the principal achievements of a program go relatively unnoticed —because they, the principals, have become an accustomed almost inherent part of the environment. In a way, this has been true of the Climate Improvement and Land Reclamation Programs. Today, people from all the nations of our World Federation travel freely to and from all corners of the globe. It is not uncommon for most of the millions of families on Earth to own two or three homes, farms, or vacation sites located on as many continents. And they commute between them as if the properties were "just down the road or up the creek." There are no restrictions to travel anywhere, no passports, no commerce or trade barriers, no customs duties or international monetary problems.

Most world citizens in our P.M.I. travel age applaud these material affluences and conveniences at great length—and little notice the uniformity of Climate and the continuous verdant beauty of all the lands that underlie their journeys.

But, of course, it is this very uniformity of Climate and agricultural excellence now spread far and wide to all lands that have made possible our opulent culture and have brought the people of the world into a "one nation" federation. No longer are there impoverished nations trying to support their citizens from terrains of frozen rock or burning sands. Nor, for more than 800 years have there been political intrigues or divergent social doctrines—whose origins were usually, and humanely, founded on a need to improve the plight of the long deprived and undernourished. The worldwide bountiful availability of the life-supportive necessities has given people of the World Federation complete freedom to expand themselves into the full-life opportunities of our Age.

One of the obvious expansions of our time is the total occupancy of the Earth's habitable terrain. Nine centuries of Land Reclamation endeavor have tripled the habitable real estate on our planet from 20th century's meager and imperfect 17,000,000 square miles to the present 47,000,000 square miles; and the remaining 10,000,000 in the Polar regions and high mountainous country are even finding partial settlement. For centuries now, world urban populations have been uncrowding themselves by moving into these new and beautiful parts of the world. In fact, the population density in several zones is still very low, and there is active competition to attract homesteaders to these more recent Land Reclamation completions.

The marvels of the P.V. (Personal Vehicular) mode of P.M.I. Propulsion have certainly played an active part in the resettlement of the world. The tens of millions of P.V. compact one-ton sedans, equipped with their snappy 1.50 GeeForce engines, easily reach 1,000 miles per hour velocity in 100 seconds. Traveling at their cruising speed of Lach 10^{-5} (1.86 miles per second or 6,700 miles per hour) on the OMNI's Raypath skyways, the P.V.'s truly have made the world into one neighborhood. On weekends, the P.V. set from all parts of the World Federation visit their vacation domiciles, so numerous for example, in the great Sahara regions or in the beautiful Australian interior—formerly the 1,500,000 square mile Great Victoria Desert—just as centuries ago, they would drive to the country to visit grandma.

Amid all of these technological sophistications there is still universally practiced the sporting rivalry of comparing the agricultural produce of one region with that from another. The golden feed grains of South America's Amazonian farms are matched against the rich cereals of South Africa's Kalahari plantations. The giant table vegetables from ancient Caspia's Kara Kum are pitted against the succulent greens raised on Canada's Hudson Bay shore. And, of course, the wines and brandies from Siberia's Yakutskaya are forever being stacked against the bouquetious *vinos cubiertos* of Argentina's Patagonian vineyards. But, it is neither really fair nor possible to assign different merit to the various regions of the world or to their products, as there is a particular excellence attached to each and every agriproduct, an excellence that matches the perfect balance of Climate and soil condition found in every land around the globe.

So that the citizen-technicians of our World Federation do not become completely and exclusively wrapped up in the satisfactions of P.M.I. travel and in their multiple, far-flung domiciles, it sometimes helps to remind that the world environment that makes these affluences possible was not always the garden that it is today. In beating the drum for EM Climate Control and the Land Reclamation Program, we recall that the Sahara was once 3,000,000 square miles of treeless, grassless void; and that its droughty wastelessness set the pattern, in a somewhat lesser degree, for more than half the surface of the Earth. The Great Western Desert of North America, embracing 1,500,000 square miles of the United States and Mexico, was once an arid wasteland and a merciless tolltaker from those who struggled to extract a livelihood from its seccacious terrain. In all of Mexico, for countless centuries, less than 10% of the land possessed a moisture, texture, or soil chemistry capable of supporting its hard-working, willing *campesinos.* And now, some 90% of that beautiful country is dotted with gleaming Standard lakes, rolling forests and plains, and bountiful family farmsteads.

During all the ages of history, the frigid vastness of ancient Siberia was, perhaps, the very source of privation. Now, Eastern Siberia's fabled Lena River Valley, with its world cultural centers of Yakutsh and Zhigansk (on the Arctic Circle), has no equal in either agricultural or industrial abundance. All of Siberia—except the Arctic fringes beyond 72 degrees North Latitude—enjoys an average 3-season temperature only 10 degrees F. cooler than the Sahara region. Many World Federation citizens reside in their Siberian villas year-round and are convinced that there is no healthier or more pleasing place in all the world. And far to the south of the happy Siberians lies the magnificent Gobi Country, a million square miles of botanical paradise in the heartlands of Mongolia and China. Ulan Bator to the north of the endless flowering desert, and Kubla Khan near Lake Ching Hai in the Nan Shan Mountains are reputed to be the most beautiful cities in the Eastern World. But once—for most of man's time and tenancy of the Earth—the Gobi was synonymous with the severity of Climatic oppression that Nature callously visited upon remote continental interiors.

Perhaps the most remarkable "before and after" of the Land Reclamation Program is the immense peninsula of Saudi Arabia, extending 1,600 miles from the Mediterranean Sea to the Indian Ocean. This most ancient of lands—capped by Biblical Assyria, Chaldea, Babylonia, and witness to the birth of "modern" human culture 11,000 years ago—was, at least during middle history, so extremely arid that less than 1% of its near 1,000,000 square miles was under cultivation. And now in our Age, since the 22nd century, mankind has seen this desert of starvation and strife transform itself into a fountain of agricultural opulence and international brotherhood. Today there is scarcely a square mile in this former sandbox that is not in orchard, pasture, or luxuriant cropland. It is a veritable Garden of Eden—which may dutifully be a second fulfillment of its historical and Biblical birthright.

TO SUMMARIZE—
A THOUSAND YEARS OF WEATHER CONTROL

The goal of Weather and Climate Control, in the vision of the EM pioneers, was to attain a moderation of the atmospheric extremes that Nature so impassively and routinely practiced. The first EM scientists, the Discoverers of the 100 EM Rayforms, knew that there must be a more reasonable, less punishing average between tempest and stagnation, between deluge and drought. At Wamsutter Weather Control Station, empowered with their new knowledge—perhaps the greatest scientific breakthrough of all time—they set out confidently, not to defy or obstruct Nature, but to encourage Her to accept the pain-relieving techniques of EM Weather Control Technology in the continuous resolution of the atmosphere's heat-balance problem. The stage for this cooperative endeavor was to be as huge as the scope and ambitions of the project—for the stage was the world itself.

Now, as we look back over the millennium, ten centuries in the Program, we are witness to a completion that must exceed even the boldest dreams of Wamsutter's pioneers. Controlled, moderated Weather; conditioned equable Climates; and 30,000,-000 square miles of Reclaimed Land are the trophies, the Wonders of the EM Weather Control Technology, shared by all the world. And—can we ever fathom why—even more than these immense material treasures have accrued to us from William Josephs' fabulous Discoveries of A.D. 1985. For, in addition to giving the world the cold mechanical processes of Weather Control and other EM Technologies, EM Science in a constantly growing presence throughout the ten centuries of our Age has evidenced what philosophical observers call an "aura"—almost a miraculous intervening—toward the recipients of its Wonders.

But, perhaps, it is more realistic to place this observation, this awareness that is shared by all men and women of our time, into its alternate sense, and to say—It is the people of the EM Age who see EM Science as more than a coincidence of our time; and who realize that it is surely a Providential gift in our behalf and on the course of our destiny.

CHAPTER II

Elemental Separators

THE EM RAYFORM TECHNOLOGY OF ELEMENTAL SEPARATION
BEAUTY BEHIND A DIRTY FACE

The fashionable and elegant sectors of our EM society and the tireless, tenacious advocates for environmental beauty agree vociferously that the EM Technology of Elemental Separation has its aesthetic limitations. There is no disputing this practical view. In fact—and in respect of it—at most of the world's OMNI stations, the monstrous piles of re-claimed sewage-and-mineral products that are the daily output of the Elemental Separation facilities are discreetly hidden behind tall, sightsaving fences. Yet, despite the grimy aspects appurtenant to its assignment, this singularly unglamourous Rayform Technology is an untiring servant; and for centuries has been not only the "clean-up" man but also the abundant supplier of the basic and raw materials that are so vital to our EM economy.

It just happens—by way of explaining its low glamour rating —that the lot of Elemental Separation has been to do our "dirty work." Its grubbing task brings it into hand-to-hand contact with the thousands of complex material compounds (and their compounded combinations) that have chemically stabilized and locked themselves within Nature. The process of Elemental Separation reduces and refines these chemical combinations—including both the natural minerals and, also, man's environmental refuse products—back to their original, formative unit elementals. In this, their separated and refined state, the elementals then become the building blocks for EM technologically guided recompositions in the manufacture of the basic industrial materials of our Age. Understandably, there is a noticeable amount of offal and smudge generated in handling these millions of tons of bulk, raw, and re-composed material.

But everything has at least a touch of beauty—so they say. And while the processes of Elemental Separation do not always grind away within a "rose garden," the fundamental workings of its Rayform technology are no less a wonder, and the Science and System behind its dirty façade are truly beautiful to behold.

ZAPSTRACTION TECHNIQUES IN
SOLUTION DE-SYNTHESIS

Scientific purists refer to them as Elemental Separators, but among the ranks of our more plain-spoken operating technicians, the sewage-and-mineral refining sections of our OMNI's are better known as Zapstractors. This sporty appellative, although implying a lack of scientific respect, is spoken with considerable professional esteem; for the history of Elemental Separation began nearly 1,000 years ago with an ancient EM technological process actually, and aptly called, Zapstraction. Pioneer EM scientists, working under the famed William Josephs in A.D. 1986 coined the descriptive nickname for their first—and peculiarly noisy— Elemental Separator, a pulsating, push-pull contrivance used for the desynthesis, or elemental breakdown, of the ionic phosphates in river water. Phosphates had become an insidious "fertilizer" in the lakes and rivers of the world, arising in the late 20th century from the widespread use of "improved" laundry detergents. The fledgling zapstraction process, made feasible by Josephs' Rayform discoveries of A.D. 1985 utilized a remarkable Rayform from the magnetic series—Rayform #31—to carry a dense magnetic attribute to the phosphate ions, therein setting them up for extraction.

Alerted, perhaps by the laundry problem, the concerned populace suddenly had become aware, and fearful, not only of the phosphate invasion, but of the portentious contamination of the total natural environment by the myriad of other metallic residues that, as an economic expedience, were being dumped into water-borne sewage disposal systems. Ecological scientists finally were heeded when they labeled some 15 ordinary metals as deadly poisonous to plant, animal, and human life—as we well know they are, in specific concentrations and associations. Chromium, mercury, arsenic, cadmium, selenium, and even common copper, lead, and zinc found themselves on the list as circumstantial poisons— particularly when they were allied with low life-form organisms in the complex bacterial-metallic digestive processes. But fortunately, the days of the metallic contaminants were short numbered, and like the errant laundry phosphates, all of them soon were to be captured and collected into giant storage piles within the yards of the Elemental Separation (Zapstraction) stations.

The A.D. 1986 solution Desynthesizer, according to EM Science archives, was no miniature indoor laboratory model. It had the appearances of a typical city-sized water supply reservoir; as indeed, it was a sprawling tank covering 40 acres with its square, mile-long outline. At the center of one sidewall of the tank there was a 10-foot bank of magnetizing anodes. And facing them from the opposite sidewall, one-quarter mile across the tank, were matching collection electrodes. Pumping facilities provided a regulated flow of test media—usually piped-in river water—across the 10-foot wide by 10-foot deep section between the two working faces. By employing a push-pull method of magnetization-extraction, the charging anodes and the collection electrodes worked in a teamed sequence to effect the Elemental Separation of the soluble (ionic) phosphates from the media. Desynthesis, as the process is officially called in EM Science archives, was accomplished by first establishing a Rayform 31 carrier path between the charging and collection piers. Onto this carrier stream, the anode (charging-side) modulation loaders superimposed the "specific magnetic attribute" of phosphate ions. Modulation (magnetic charging) time was 5 micro-seconds, the push half of the cycle. At the cutoff instant of magnetic charging, the opposite-side collection electrodes commenced an equal 5 micro-second gathering

action, the pull phase. Phosphate ions, magnetically influenced
by the charging path, attached themselves to the gathering-phase
carriers and, at close to speed-of-light velocity, were carried into
the collection chutes. Here, magnetic "deattribution" (demodula-
tion) of the phosphate ions, produced the deposition of solid
state elemental *materia*. In this particular situation, the deposited
phosphate ions (PO^4) spontaneously reverted to nascent oxygen
and phosphorus, a separation that was then preserved and
stabilized within the collection tunnels.

The charging action of the carrier stream during the push
phase and the movement of the captured ions on their Rayform
31 carriers in the pull phase created very little physical distur-
bance in the tank, the carrier propagation being similar to the
passage of ordinary light through a liquid media. But, needless
to say, as the invisible phosphates from the river solution under-
went direct transition into solid-state form and product at the
crude collection chutes of that original Desynthesizer, there must
have been a fierce—although somewhat musical—"szapping"
sound. Since this first Solution Desynthesizer was principally an
extractor, we speculate that the pioneer technicians, perhaps with
a few smiles, combined the noise and the function to name their
machine, the Zapstractor.

The Technology of Elemental Separation has come a long and
progressive way since the Zapstractor of A.D. 1986. Today,
almost every compounded material in Nature finds itself subjected to elemental refinement and recomposition by the machinery
of EM E/S Technology. Modern Elemental Separation plants
operate at remarkable efficiencies, and in almost complete silence
using full-time, controlled-rate on-and-off phasing during the
charging, the gathering, and the *materia* transition stages. That
"sweet szapping sound," characteristic of sudden ionic transition
in the solution desynthesis process, and so familiar in the old
push-pull zapstractors, has long been just another nostalgic
recording from early times. But while its "szap" may have
bowed to the centuries of technological progress, its revered nickname—Zapstraction—remains for all time to recall the adventure

and excitement that must have surrounded the pioneer EM scientist-technicians in their noisy, 20th century beginning of Elemental Separation Technology.

SPECIFIC MAGNETIC CHARGE
MAGNETIC NUMBERS AND THEIR ORDERS

The EM principle that is the scientific foundation for the Technology of Elemental Separation is best explained in terms of the natural phenomenon known as the "Specific Magnetic Charge" of an element. This distinguishing property of every elemental material (or isotropic form of the material) is a function related to its Magnetic Number, a categorizing assignment similar to the Atomic Number and Atomic Weight designations fixed to each element. While every element has a popularly known, definitive Specific Magnetic Charge, there are usually several other levels—or orders—of the Charge, each of which conveys a different physical attribute to the element. These various levels of Magnetic Charge correspond to the exponential ratios, better known as the orders of Magnetic Number. EM Science has not only brought to light the phenomenon of Specific Magnetic Charge and Number but it has also given us the amazing "30" series of Rayforms (R-30 through R-39), which have the wondrous capability to carry the orders of Magnetic Number to targeted elementals and to their ionic radical forms. In Elemental Separation applications, these 30-series Rayform carriers are programmed to convey magnetic (and other) properties—corresponding to the orders—at controlled additive and subtractive rates to match the particular materials and the technological objectives.

First order Magnetic Numbers represent the Magnetic Charge that elements exhibit in their natural, everyday, stabilized state. A few of the elements, iron and cobalt for example, demonstrate conventional magnetism in their elemental and even in some of their compounded natural forms. But generally, first order Magnetic Numbers are not effective in causing most materials, as they occur in our normal Earthly environment to display measureable magnetic properties. The EM Discoveries, however, show that nearly every element will exhibit magnetic effect when influenced by its particular 30-series Rayform, carrying the third, fifth, or seventh order of the element's Magnetic Number. These *odd* harmonic orders are best propagated in liquid solutions, where the targeted elementals exist in their soluble, ionic forms. Every ionic solution group, whether it be an elemental or a compounded chemical radical form—such as the phosphate, sulfate, carbonate, or hydroxide—has a characteristic Magnetic Number and readily becomes magnetized when subjected to the stress of one of the odd harmonics of its Number.

EM Science, since the dawn of our Age, has given man an ever-broadening field of understanding of the properties and physical "constants" of *materia*. It has shown us the role that Magnetic Number—in its total spectra—plays in determining not only the magnetic, but several of the nonmagnetic properties that materials manifest. Among these common nonmagnetic properties, controlled by the *even*-order influences of Magnetic Number, are color, hardness, viscosity, ductility, and malleability. It should be noted, as a point of accuracy, that Rayforms outside the 30-series also serve as efficient carriers of many other of the nonmagnetic attributes of materials. (In this context—the nonmagnetic influences of Magnetic Number—the term Magnetic Number is a misnomer; and exacting authorities refer to the even-order Numbers as the *Non*magnetic Numbers.)

But the role of the even-order Magnetic Numbers, in itself, is a separate and another intriguing story in EM Science; and somewhat off our present course. Our subject task, the study of the application of the odd-order Magnetic Numbers to the Technology of Elemental Separation, is adequately confining. In this restriction, then, we will review some of the pioneer installations of Elemental Separators, in order to gain a comprehension of the general principles of their design and operation. These EM scientific principles have persisted since their Discovery 1,000 years ago, and still apply today in our clean-up, refinement, and redistribution of the materials necessary to modern life and to the EM economy.

MARIETTA, OHIO U.S.A.
THE FIRST CROSS-RIVER ELEMENTAL SEPARATION
STATIONS

With the announcement of the Great EM Discoveries of A.D. 1985 America's Science Advisory Council named Elemental Separation as one of the three Rayform Technologies that were to be developed at forced effort, for presentation to the world nations in A.D. 2000. Weather Control and P.M.I. (Projected Magnetic Image) Propulsion were the two other EM Technologies selected to prove and to demonstrate the realities and the wonders of the Discoveries—and to show how EM Science could be a key to the achievement of peace, prosperity, and world harmony. Thus it was, at Marietta, Ohio, U.S.A., in the historic millennial year A.D. 2000 that the first Cross-River Elemental Separator was put "on stream" to fulfill a technological as well as an awesome political mission.

The Science Advisory Council chose Marietta as the development site for Elemental Separation because the city was geographic host to two environmentally plagued rivers—the meandering southerly flowing Muskingum, and its confluent receiver, the majestic Ohio. The smaller Muskingum was to serve as the site for an exact 10% engineering prototype of the larger Cross-River plant that was to be building concurrently, though with a 10-year later completion date, on the half-mile wide Ohio. And this, in fact, was the sequence of construction at the Marietta stations. Muskingum #1, 10 miles upstream from the city, met its maximum effort construction schedule to become the millennial year demonstrator for E/S Technology. Today, world famous Marietta International Park includes both Cross-River facilities, Muskingum #1 and Ohio River #1. Together they share the honor and tribute as the birthplace of Elemental Separation. And though they have been modernized many times during the past 10 centuries, both stations are still in daily operation on their original foundations.

Ohio River #1, placed on stream in A.D. 2010 incorporated many design refinements gained from the proximate operational experience of its 10% scale model. To the immediate benefit of Ohio River #1, and also to the ultimate enhancement of the thousands of subsequent E/S stations, Muskingum #1 carried on an expeditious testing and mechanical de-bugging of the Rayform C-M-A (Converter-Magnetizer-Accelerator) units, the Rayform Pulse Projection units, and the Magnetic Number Modulation Loaders used in large Elemental Separation installations. Pierhead anode and collection-electrode designs were markedly improved at Muskingum #1 in the few short years that the tributary station operated as proving ground for the new Technology. By using Muskingum's experience in anode and electrode design, the builders of Ohio River #1 were able to install dual-purpose pierheads, capable of either magnetic charging or ionic collection, on both the Ohio and West Virginia sides of the river. Dual-purpose pierhead capability would prove to be a valuable foresight; for soon after Ohio River #1 went on stream, the tremendous tonnages of extracted materials created a crushing logistics problem; more than could be handled by a single-sided collection yard.

Each of the pierheads of Ohio River #1 presented a 100-foot-long working face parallel to the river flowline. The opposing structures were separated by a cross-river span of 1,500 feet. By means of massive concrete shoreline diking and cross-stream profile contouring, a working depth of 10 feet was maintained across the Ohio's modified bed. When operated at its designed extraction rate of 100 tons of elemental material per hour from a liquid flow of 10^6 (one million) tons, the station equipment including the C-M-A, required only 1,000 KW of electrical power. During Springtime flood conditions, river flow could exceed by several times the one million ton per hour, or 4 million gallons per minute, media-flow capacity of the station. But, under these seasonal conditions, contaminant concentrations would be proportionally diluted; and even so, would eventually be totally extracted by the combined efforts of other E/S facilities planned for the interior waterway systems in this region of the United States. At Ohio River #1, pulsed Zapstraction techniques were used, with the push-pull orientations controllable to or from either side of the river. The plant's magnetizing, gathering, and ionic-to-solid transition machinery was designed to select any of 100 different elemental ionic materials; and was capable of a simultaneous extraction program in 10 separate Elemental working channels.

The principal environmental-refuse additives found in the Ohio River in that era, and the ones to which the E/S machinery were usually keyed, were the phosphates, sulfates, chlorates, and some 18 metallic ions including those of iron, copper, lead, mercury, potassium, and sodium. Strontium and 9 other systems of radioactive contaminants could be captured when and if their concentration became a health hazard. Two of the 10 working channels were tunable to the system of complex bacterial organisms and were effective in sludging out many persistent-type endotoxins. Following the inauguration of Ohio River #1, downstream users of the Ohio were assurred of not only cleaner, but also, healthier water.

At the collection chutes on both the Ohio and West Virginia sides, transitionalized ionic materials were processed according to the natural inclinations of their chemistries. Those that are stable in the elemental state, such as iron, copper, and lead, were retained as elements and transported to storage or directly to commercial disposition. Those that innately seek chemical re-combination, such as the fluorines and chlorines, phosphorus, sodium, and potassium were processed either through Elemental State Preservers where they were stabilized and containerized for subsequent distribution and re-use in the economy—or they were combined with huge quantities of ordinary country silicates and carbonates (sand, soil, and rock) to become desirable types of enriched concentrates for replacement in the agriculture.

This first of the large Cross-River Elemental Separator plants generated an amount of re-claimed product of a quality and in quantities that forecast rapid and revolutionary changes for the world economy. The 100-acre storage yards behind each pierhead became beehives of material handling activity. Operating at its full extraction rate of 100 tons per hour, Ohio River #1 imposed a noticeable load on the transportation industry in the area. Blending carbonates and silicates used in the product re-combination processes had to be shipped in, as well as out, adding another 200 tons per hour to the plant's material traffic. By A.D. 2020 a substantial percentage of the 300-ton-per-hour bulk volume was being carried in new EM Transport low-altitude freighters, powered by P.M.I. (Projected Magnetic Image) engines perfected within the prior decade. Mining, manufacturing, and transportation industries in that 21st century dawning of the EM Age were all undergoing change to adapt to the economic revolution posed by the Cross-River Elemental Separator and its bounteous products.

The early and almost shocking success of the Ohio River plant, both as an environmental clean-up agent and as a material resource generator, stimulated the construction of hundreds of Elemental Separators on the river and lake systems on all the continents. In the U.S.A. within the decade from A.D. 2010 to A.D. 2020, cross-river plants were completed at 10 locations on the Mississippi-Missouri, at 6 sites on the Hudson River, at 10 cities on the smaller rivers in industrial New England, at 4 on the Delaware, 10 at the larger rivers of the western states, and at one important site on the Detroit River south of that city. Plans had been drawn by this time to install Cross-River Elemental Separators on every navigable river around the globe, wherever a spoliation of Nature was threatened—or in combination with, the commercially advantageous extraction of particular indigenous minerals.

CROSS-LAKE ELEMENTAL SEPARATORS— MICHIGAN and ERIE—A.D. 2030

In a bold and interesting extension of the Technology, two Cross-Lake Elemental Separators became operational by A.D. 2030. These lake-scrubbing facilities utilized narrow-band Rayform carrier paths in a 10 to 1 technological exchange of cross-sectional saturation for linear range. But in all other specifications, the equipments were identical to those of the Cross-River plants. The first of the Cross-Lakers spanned the southern end of Lake Michigan, enclosing within its sweep all the waters contiguous to greater Chicago. The installation had its westerly pierhead on Evanston Point, Illinois, and its easterly working face was 48 open-water miles distant at Michigan City, Indiana. Natural lake currents slowly, but continually, flushed the "loaded" waters of the Chicago sector back and forth across the activated Northwest-Southeast Rayform path. Within 10 years, offshore Chicago and the entire body of Lake Michigan were returned to a "pure water" classification.

The other pioneer Cross-Lake Elemental Separator spanned an equal 48 miles in Lake Erie between Avon Point, Ohio, and Rondeau Point, Ontario, Canada. In spite of the great span, but aided by the relatively shallow character of Erie, this first internationally shared "Zapstractor" brought noticeable improvement to the lake's water quality within two short years. Natural currents, in a scheme similar to the Chicago-Lake Michigan Project, were utilized to circulate the lake burden across the one-foot wide Rayform charging-gathering path. After five years of operation, in A.D. 2035, the Lake Erie E/S plant was adjusted to magnetize-and-gather only 10 miles out from each shore, the middle portion of the lake having been reduced to its native purity.

A side benefit from Erie's Avon-Rondeau Elemental Separator was the generation of huge quantities of calcium from the limestone-rich waters. The calcium, like all Elementally Separated products, was of the finest purity and was eagerly sought after by the revitalized Portland cement industries of both Ohio and Ontario. In a pattern that typified the industrial expansion that accompanied all E/S facilities, major cement manufacturing plants sprang up near the pierhead collection yards on both sides of the lake. Using an innovative process dependent on the abundant availability of elemental calcium—and described as the direct exothermic recombination of calcium, silica, and alumina—the new cement makers became the first to produce Portlands that imparted a steel-like machinability and flexibility to structural concrete.

The 48-mile-long Rayform 30 paths across Lake Michigan and Lake Erie were completely unnoticeable; and even the silent charging-gathering "action" of the activated spans could not be detected by a human swimmer who might venture across them. On and below the lake surface there was neither turbulence nor any mysterious or injurious effect to human life or to the fish in the area. Not surprisingly, within 10 years of the initial operation of both pioneer Cross-Lake plants, great schools of pickerel, blue pike, and yellow perch returned and abounded in the lakes, as they had existed prior to the impairment of those waters by indiscriminate dumping in the recent 20th century.

[It is interesting to note that integral life-forms—such as animals, fishes, and whole plants—have a protective immunity from the 30 series Rayforms, which seem to prefer to travel around but not through large life-forms. In this regard, it has always been extremely difficult—even if it were to be physiologically useful—to magnetize the human body or other large life forms. Magnetic effect appears to be restricted to the lifeless materials and to the extreme low-life micro-organisms, generally classified as bacteria.]

But while Cross-Lake Rayform paths are invisible, there is one startling exception that was discovered soon after the Lake Erie facility went on stream. Because of the unusual amount of ionic calcium in Erie's Rayform track, there occurs a visual radiance phenomenon called "Calcescence"—or ionic calcium mirage. Astonishingly, terrestrial objects in a calcescent state are visible only from outer space, far above and beyond the Earth's atmosphere. Lake Erie's calcescent Rayform path shows up in space as a brilliant arrow-straight, blue-violet line. Its visible emission characteristics appear to defy the rules of normal light, in that its perceived brilliance harmonically increases and decreases —not unlike a desert's mirage—at specific intervals of space. The settlers on Earth's moon, as well as space voyagers everywhere, never cease in their amazement at being able, on occasion, to sight Lake Erie's "calcium line" from their great distances.

SOLUBILITY CONTROL
AN E/S TECHNOLOGICAL BREAKTHROUGH

Although now in our modern time, the use of extremely high-energy magnetizers can be employed to extract elementals from solid state ores and mineral-rich soils, it has always been—for the past 10 centuries—more efficient and practical to design Elemental Separators for service in liquid (ionic solution) media. The superiority of liquid-state Separators was doubly and firmly established in the final years of the 21st century, when scientists of the U.N. EM Science Council discovered the key to increasing a material's solubility (and ionization) in both ordinary fresh and salt water solvents. These findings led to the development of Ionic-Rate Solubility Control Equipments, which were immediately integrated into Elemental Separator designs. Improved Separators, utilizing Selective Solution Expediters, were able to extract at least 10-fold greater production tonnages of the hitherto "insoluble" metals. The new designs found ready assignment in the many slurry type mining plants at inland and mountainous sites—most of the heavy-metal ores are poor natural dissolvers. But the greatest impact of the improved solubility techniques was in the operation of ocean-site Elemental Separator and Extractor plants.

The magnesium Extractor at Corpus Christi, Texas, is illustrative of the great change in capability that came with the addition of Solubility Control to the original Elemental Separator at that site. Selective Solution Expediter auxiliaries at Corpus Christi, not only exposed larger amounts of ionic magnesium to the working stream but they also, indirectly, worked on the ageless depths of mineral sediment on the floor of the sea, to provoke the mag-compounded muds and rockbeds into aqueous solution. Thus, an unlimited—almost perpetual—reserve of mineral became available to feed the extraction process.

Solubility Control also, of course, caused a marked increase in the propagation or conductivity characteristics of the Rayform carriers along their curved cross-water spans. The original Corpus Christi plant, placed in operation in A.D. 2050, had an extraction capacity of 100 tons of magnesium, or titanium, per hour, and worked a 10-mile curved track of Gulf water between pierheads on Mustang and St. Joseph islands. After the facility redesign in A.D. 2090, and by virtue of improved Rayform conductivity, Corpus Christi was capable of projecting its charging-gathering carriers outward in immense elliptical patterns with maximum reaches of 500 miles. At its extreme sweep, the Rayform path tapped the immense alluvial deposits of the Mississippi delta on the north, and the Yucatan shoals on the south. Extraction capacity of the Corpus Christi plant jumped to 1,000 tons per hour, yielding more magnesium than the Western Hemisphere could use in that era. Consequently, the operation was split between the production of magnesium and titanium, until A.D. 2600 when decreased world demand for magnesium switched the production schedule entirely to titanium. The Corpus Christi plant operates today on this single elemental assignment, and its present technology and physical design are not much different from what they were following the historical Solubility Control improvements in A.D. 2090.

GOLD—A NEW STANDARD—FOR ROOFS

Another remarkable Elemental Separator installation, one that curiously and interestingly upset all the monetary regulations of the world, was built by the Russians in A.D. 2095. We read in history that man, from the earliest recorded times, has been a collector, and often a hoarder, of the common roofing metal we call gold. Not too many centuries ago nations actually stored bars of this soft yellow metal in guarded vaults and used it as a backing for their paper money. The metal was considered quite valuable, paradoxically, only because of its scarcity. It has poor dynamic and strength imparting qualities and is not highly regarded in present-day technical circles, other than for the fact that it is suited to the waterproofing of rooftops. At any rate and with a glorious finality, the myth of gold was dissolved in A.D. 2095 when the U.S.S.R. Severnaya Zemlya plant went on stream.

The "Sev-Zem" Siberian Extraction station on the 100th meridian east and the 80th parallel north, reached out into the vast Arctic Ocean to tap deposits of gold that Mother Earth had been flushing into the Arctic during millions of year of continental erosion. The design of Sev-Zem was similar to that of the Corpus Christi Mag-Titanium facility. Using the remarkable new Selective Solution Expediter tuned for gold, the Siberian Extractor spanned out elliptically more than 700 miles to sweep the floors of the Arctic Ocean as far away as the North Pole. During its very first year of extraction at a rated output of more than 100 tons per hour, the plant yielded close to 10^6 (one million) tons of the yellow metal. This production achievement amounted to more than 30 times all the gold that man had mined from the Earth during all of previous history.

Other gold-extraction Elemental Separators soon followed the Siberian installation. Ocean-working plants in Iceland, on the Falkland Islands in the South Atlantic, in New Zealand, and at Point Barrow, Alaska, each reclaimed from the sea an annual tonnage nearly equal to that of the U.S.S.R.'s Arctic station. At the turn of the century, in A.D. 2100, gold had become so plentiful and inexpensive that already it was being widely used in housing construction as roof flashings, rain gutters, and downspouts—although its application in these categories was considered by many titanium-oriented architects to be more decorative than efficacious. But gold's extremely low cost and its facility for being formed into leakproof leafing favored its selection, and its popular use, in shingle pattern, as the common complete roofing material.

Gold, the "inviolable" monetary backing for worldwide trade, had lost all status by this time. Its value as money was doomed, in any event, by the formation fo the United World Federation—the single "nation" of the world. By A.D. 2050 the new UWF currency had begun to phase out and replace the multiplicity of moneys of the world nations. Under control of the UWF Federal Reserve Board, made up of representatives from all lands, UWF currency was issued to each state in amounts equivalent to the maximum, but non-inflationary economic capabilities of that member state. In the spirit of mutual trust and cooperation that was the cornerstone of the United World Federation—and of the worldwide participation in EM Science and Technology—UWF currency was backed, simply, by acknowledgement notes tendered to the Federal Reserve by the member states. The flood of gold that followed from the Severnya Zemyla and other gold-producing Elemental Separators expedited the phasing out of the remaining gold-backed monetary systems in the world. In fact, in A.D. 2100 the U.S.S.R., last world state to hold onto partially gold-backed currency, released all of her bullion to roofing manufacturers and wholeheartedly joined the United World Federation Federal Reserve Board. From that time on, UWF currency has been the single, universal money of the world.

EM ELEMENTAL SEPARATORS TODAY

In our present step in time—as modern man approaches A.D. 3000—it is estimated that there are more than a billion Elemental Separators on stream in all corners of the Earth. They range in size from the one- and two-pound per hour household miniatures to the giant 10,000-ton-per-hour oceangoing dredges. Every industrial and commercial complex, and every population center of 1,000 people has its 100-ton unit-community E/S facility. Some of these are assigned full time to sanitation and sewage service; others have sundry added tasks in the extraction of undesirable chemistries, and in preventing local effluents from infringement, downstream, on the habitational rights of neighbors. Ionic air-and-gas scrubbers—vapor state variations of the more efficient liquid-state Elemental Separators—have long been in common use in industry, where smokes and vaporous residues have been matters of concern.

Thousands of large cross-river, lakeshore, and ocean-site Separators with nominal ratings of 1,000 tons per hour have been supplying all the world's basic metallic needs, and—by Elemental Re-Composition—most of the raw non-metallic compounded inorganics. Many of these world-circling stations boast of founding dates that go far back into 21st and 22nd century pioneer EM times. Although all of these large separators have broad technological flexibility, with any one installation being capable of processing a hundred or more different elementals simultaneously, it has been more efficient and practical to tailor operations at individual plants to take advantage of nearby natural resource concentrations. In the past four or five centuries, therefore, most of these 1,000-ton landmark E/S facilities have been on specific mineral assignment, usually with only one or two elementals as their extraction target. The variety of recomposition products is also held to a minimum at every station. However, it often happens that the final product of an E/S supplier is represented by several alloyed combinations based on the principal extracted elemental.

Corpus Christi, for example, works only on titanium and its Re-Composition into alloyed slabs of some 20 different chemistries, bearing various and minute percentages of platinum, silver, and boron. Each of the alloyed titaniums is earmarked to become a particular functional component in a P.M.I. Heavy Transport vessel, whose production in nearby Texas industrial centers is closely tied to the titanium Extraction plant. Corpus Christi, with its annual gross of 8 million tons, is just one of a hundred Separators located around the globe that account for current annual production of 800 million tons of this most widely used structural metal of our EM Age—an age that is sometimes narrowly, but rightly called the Titanium Age.

Cape Town, South Africa, another typical 1,000-ton-per-hour ocean-site Separator, extracts the single elemental, vanadium, from its 2,000-mile southerly reaches that touch the shores of Antarctica. Vanadium, alloyed with small amounts (1 to 5 percent) of iron, still finds application in the construction of heavy machinery designed for Ultimate Pressure Processes, the metal flow-forming technology of modern industry.

Antofagasta, Chile, sends its Rayform-30 paths westward more than 2,500 miles into the Pacific, to draw upon the vast Easter Island Undersea Cordillera for basic zirconium, diamacious carbon, and sapphiritic aluminum. The Re-Composition product from Antofagasta—ZDS (Zircon, Diamond, and Sapphire) refractory is ideally suited to lining and relining the acceleration tunnels in the millions of C-M-A's (Converter-Magnetizer-Accelerator) in which Rayforms, themselves, are constituted for use in our technologies.

The Japanese furnish 60% of the world's Iridium needs from their ocean-site E/S Station at Kushiro, Hokkaido. And the Ceylonese at Colombo, on the Island of Ceylon, sweep the equatorial waters of the Indian Ocean from the African coast on the west to Sumatra on the east in their search for platinum, columbium, and tantalum; the latter two elementals so especially vital to the newest EM Technology, which enables the Condensation and Storage of GRAVITY from the depths of the Milky Way Galaxy.

And there are so many more. But it would be impossible in this brief accounting to mention the names and locations of all of these famous large Extractors; except to say that each has its own interesting story in our industrial history, and each station continues every day and hour to fulfill its specific, important assignment in our worldwide coordinated economy. All operational activities of these great facilities find themselves programmed and regulated by the World Federation Basic-Resource Computer— the cybernetic implemental arm of the industrial technologists who make up the World Federation Economic Board. There is no waste and neither excessive nor short productive rates to disturb the efficient, calculated pace of world commerce and industry. And because of the great expanses of ocean covered by the sweeps of the ocean-site mineral Extractors, reserve resources of the minerals needed to support the EM economy appear to be inexhaustible, within the scope of man's present need—on this planet—for them.

Despite the prodigious achievements of the thousands of large cross-river, cross-lake, and ocean-site Separators, there is still a much larger and possibly harder-working group of Elemental Separators. These, of course, are the standard 1,000-ton-per-hour E/S Centrals, located in the 750,000 EM OMNI Stations around the globe. Each of these master Elemental Separator facilities—and there is one for every 10-mile × 10-mile OMNI-covered square of inhabited land or sea on the face of the Earth—functions as the coordinator and monitor of all the dependent Separators within its area. Most of the smaller outlying Elemental Separators in a typical 100 square mile OMNI service area are incomplete installations; usually not equipped with C-M-A's for Rayform Constitution, nor with Elemental Re-Composition plants to process and dispose of their separated, elemental products. For these essential services, the outlying dependents rely on their E/S Centrals. By means of Short-Arc C-M-A Broadcast technique, an

E/S Central transmits a full band of 30-series Rayforms to the hundreds, and sometimes even thousands, of dependent Separators under its management. The receiving dependent installation merely tunes in its assigned Rayform carrier for the task at hand, at a controlled quantitative rate, applies its local-task specific magnetic attribute, and is in the Elemental Separation business. And, as a product disposer, every E/S Central is quite well known—even to the point of being submerged, sometimes, by the excesses of good-natured attention—for its "honey barge" fleet of Short-Haul P.M.I. airtrucks that pick up extracted elementals from the many scattered household and unit-community Elemental Separators.

E/S Centrals usually assume responsibility for all of the Elemental Re-Composition and final product distribution within their 100 square mile authorities—except for that which may be handled by a large independent Separator in the area. In addition to the never-ending workload originating with their external dependents, E/S Centrals also operate as working Elemental Separators, handling a myriad of internal assignments for component technologies of the OMNI station. They perform countless extraction, qualifying, and purifying tasks for the Weather and Climate Control Section, the Rayform 10 Direct Current Electric Power Net, the Rayform 17 Water Supply System, the Gravity Storage and Distribution Section, the P.M.I. Aerospace Vessel Raypath Guidance Section, and others. The role of E/S Centrals in the World Land Reclamation Program—made possible by the EM Weather and Climate Control Systems—has been a key factor in opening to mankind more than 30,000,000 square miles of habitable, productive land, an area greater than half the total land surface of the Earth. The soil enhancement ingredients, in tonnages beyond the imagination, that have been used in the reconstitution of those former deserts and wastelands have come primarily from our old and reliable housekeepers, the Elemental Separator Centrals in the OMNI's circling the globe. They have been working steadily on this mammoth project for more than 900 years, since EM Weather Control and EM Elemental Separation teamed up to serve all the people of the Earth.

The Technology of Elemental Separation has been at work on

the Earth's moon dating from the first lunestrial settlement in
A.D. 2070. Today on the Moon there are some 1,300 OMNI
Stations, each with its 100 channel Elemental Separator, located
on the dual 10-mile × 10-mile Green Belts that circle the 6,500-
mile equatorial circumference. Earth-Moon colonists, now number-
ing 250,000 men, women, and children, live in Earth-like comfort
on the once-desolate giant satellite. And even farther out in
space, Elemental Separators as components of the OMNI's are
making life tolerable for our pioneer colonizers of the moon
Rhea of Saturn, and on Ganymede of Jupiter.

*   *   *

The EM Technology with the dirt smudges on its face, and
with the bulging backyards that hide behind tall, sight-saving
fences, need never be ashamed of appearances. For what Wonder
of EM Science can boast of so great a concern and munificence
toward its beholders—who, in genuine esteem, recognize the deep
and true beauty of Elemental Separation.

CHAPTER III

P.M.I. (Projected Magnetic Image) Propulsion

FROM THE ARCHIVES OF EM HISTORY

We are fortunate that the Archives of EM History set forth in clear detail the events surrounding the Discovery of the EM Rayforms. Particularly, we place high value on the Archival section that describes the Discoveries in conjunction with the initial presentation of the Technology of P.M.I. (Projected Magnetic Image) Propulsion. This chapter from EM History is extra special in that it brings us closer than does any other recorded account to the person of William Josephs, the venerable founder of our Age. It reveals also the urgency of the political and social crises of that time, in the closing decades of the 20th century, and it shows the lifesaving role that the new science was able to relate to these problems. Authored—it is certain—by William Josephs himself, this section of the Archives explains in simple and plausible terms the fundamentals of EM Rayform Science. From it, too, we learn something of the motivations, the long years of research, and the ultimate success that the pioneers experienced. In its technical message, it introduces us to the Wonder of EM Science that, more than any other, challenges our inhibited human conceptual abilities—our limited imaginations. Here then, is the story of the Wonder of P.M.I. Propulsion, based upon the original version in the Archives of EM History.

A HISTORIC ASSEMBLY AND ASSIGNMENT
PLUM BROOK, OHIO A.D. 1985

In the spring of A.D. 1985, America's Presidential Science
Advisory Council met in historic assembly with 300 of the world's
leading scientists at the NASA Propulsion Research Laboratory
in Plum Brook, Ohio, U.S.A. This extraordinary convention of
renowned intellectuals, all of whom were as enthusiastic and
excited as schoolboys over the recently announced EM Scientific
Discoveries, included among its participants 100 of the U.S.A.'s
NASA scientists, 100 other American scientists and engineers
principally from the aerospace industries, and 100 men and
women of science and industry, representing the technologically
advanced nations of the 20th-century world. Each honored guest
had come at the personal invitation of the United States President,
Thomas Carlos Corigan.

During the preceding three months, since New Year's Day
of A.D. 1985, the American Science Advisory Council had been
in continuous session with William Josephs and other pioneer EM
scientists to witness and to receive the disclosure of the spectacular EM Scientific Discoveries. On February 25 of that celebrated
year, the Council, together with the President of the United
States and the Founder of EM Science, announced to the world
a broad and general description of the amazing EM Discoveries.
As experts in every field of scientific knowledge, the members of
the President's Council, of course, were quick to grasp an understanding of the EM Rayform Breakthrough and of the astounding
technological possibilities that the Discoveries heralded. But, in
an altruistic and philanthropic spirit, the concerned men of this
American Council also sensed the influence that EM Science and
its consequent technologies could have upon the world's social
and political structures. This era, the late 20th century, was a
time in history under the shadow of grave international political
differences. The extremes of these differences, and the monstrous
military establishments that supported them, were cause for many
informed citizens of that day to resign themselves—both in a

nationalistic and in a personal sense—to a future without hope. It truly was an ominous time, one that forebode the destruction of the human race, an inevitable cataclysm that man had become capable of bringing down on himself by an indiscriminate, maniacally prompted military abuse of the terrible force of nuclear energy. And the trigger for this sad demise of mankind was located in any one of a thousand ICBM launch sites around the globe.

In A.D. 1985, when the EM Discoveries arrived on this confused, disconsolate world scene, America's Science Advisory Council jubilantly welcomed them. For, in their deep and prospecting wisdom, the members of the Council saw the new Discoveries as a means, even as a Providential torch, to guide the troubled, mistrusting world back to sanity and to its own survival. These American guardians of Science, the first men favored to receive William Josephs' fabulous gift, realized that the EM Discoveries could bring forward a total technological revolution whose products and systems would serve all the world in an abundance beyond concept. They foresaw changes and achievements for mankind so extensive and rewarding that, in a contemporary comparison, all the social, political, and nationalistic goals of the American people, as well as the goals of all the world nations, would become lost in their own triviality and insignificance. Thus it was, under these portentous social and political circumstances in the spring of 1985 at Plum Brook, Ohio, that there convened an assembly with two motivating purposes—one Scientific, the other Humanitarian—but both of which were crucial to the future of man on Earth. America's leaders held the prayerful hope that the representatives from the many world nations, just as the President's Science Advisory Council had done, would contemplate the opportunities, and more importantly, the necessity to direct the utilization of the new EM Science and its Technologies toward the achievement of a peaceful and harmonious coexistence among all the peoples and nations of the world.

As its specific scientific purpose, the Plum Brook meeting served to introduce publicly a remarkable dynamic Technology derived from the EM Rayform Breakthrough. This almost incredible

application of the new EM Science was known from that time on
—even as we call it today—as Projected Magnetic Image Propulsion, or P.M.I. Propulsion. The President's representative at
Plum Brook, Dr. Terrell E. Whiteacre, Chairman of the Science
Advisory Council, chose to present P.M.I. Propulsion to the
world in conjunction with the announcement of a challenging
assignment to the NASA. The National Aeronautics and Space
Agency, in association with the aerospace industries of America,
was given the mandate by Dr. Whiteacre to begin an immediate
development, and to have in operation by the year A.D. 2000,
100 prototype aerospace craft powered by P.M.I. Propulsion.
The 100 P.M.I.-Propelled prototypes were to have combined
atmospheric and outer-space full-time operational capabilities. The
assignment called for the construction of category types in the
four fields of Heavy Transport, Medium and Light Commercial,
and Personal Vehicular. Ten special models were to be designed
for extended-period deep-space exploration and were to be equipped
with year-long living quarters for 10 resident scientists in addition
to an equal complement of ship's company technicians.

At this stage in our story of the early development of P.M.I.
Propulsion, it is interesting to note the systematic approach
expressed in the selection of vessel gross-weight capacities and
propulsion capabilities. As we have observed in all of the activities
of the pioneers of our Age, there was an obvious concern for
oncoming generations, and for the ultimate futuristic utilizations
of the new Technology. In this long-range plan and pattern—
Heavy Transport vessels had gross weight specifications of 1,000
tons, and P.M.I. Propulsion full-time-continuous ratings of 1.01
GeeForce. Medium Commercial types were a 10% (1 to 10)
version of the Heavy Transports, with gross weight schedules of
100 ton, but with P.M.I. Propulsion units up-rated to 1.10 Gee-
Force. In further gross-weight 10% design decrements, Light
Commercial vessels weighted in at 10 ton, and Personal Vehicular
sedans at only 1 ton. Both of these lighter categories were equipped
with high performance 1.50 GeeForce P.M.I. Propulsion units.
The 10 special space research vessels were to be similar in
configuration to the 100-ton Medium Commercials, except that

their **P.M.I.** units were to be capable of 3.03 GeeForce, an amount deemed necessary for entry-and-exit operations in the vicinity of giant Jupiter. In addition to their main P.M.I. Propulsion units, every one of the 100 prototype vessels was to be equipped with a stand-by P.M.I. unit whose non-continuous 1.50 GeeForce rating could usually and normally effect a safe Earth return in the event of main P.M.I. failure.

[GeeForce ratings are always stated in values relative to the vessels that they propel. Thus, a nominal 1.01 GeeForce P.M.I. system in a Heavy Transport is capable of imparting velocity to the craft by means of P.M.I. Propulsion in a degree of effort that will accelerate the 1,000-ton vessel at 1.01 g.—or 1/100th of, and in addition to, the acceleration due to Earth gravity (32.2 feet per second per second at 55 degrees Latitude at sea level elevation). In conventional gravitational force units, 1.01 Gee-Force acting on a 1,000-ton vessel will develop a thrust of 1,010 tons, or 101% of the gravity force (weight) on the vessel.

Nominal GeeForce ratings are full-time continuous values. Short-time GeeForce ratings are considerably higher than the nominal nameplate ratings. Short-time ratings range from the One-Hour E.E.P. (Emergency Effort Propulsion) of 5 times nominal GeeForce, to the Sixty-Hour P.E.P. (Prolonged Effort Propulsion) of 3 times nominal. It is customary—in fact, mandatory—today, to use only nominal GeeForce throttle settings on all conventional commutation and excursion flights. EM Raypath Guidance Traffic Control Authority is absolute in enforcing this P.M.I. skypath operational precept. E.E.P. (5 ×) and P.E.P. (3 ×) short-time ratings are reserved for emergency discretions only.

Although it is generally understood by all EM Age people, it may be an aid in point of technical comprehension to remind that neither the exhaustion of propulsion energy reserve nor the depletion of on-board fuel are relevant to the performance of ordinary P.M.I. flights or to vessel gross weights. Even in pioneer days, P.M.I. Propulsion units had full-time-continuous GeeForce capacities for 10^5 hours (more than 10 years) without need for replacement of their fuel-energy cells.]

The rapid progress of P.M.I. Technology and the high production rate of P.M.I. aerospace vessels during the 1st century of our Age are attributed to the standardizations of vessel design established by the A.D. 1985 Science Council. The Council's initial decision to order four categorical types, differing by exact 0-1-2-3 logarithmic integers of 10—with each of the four gross-weight designs powered by a sensibly and practically-sized P.M.I. Gee-Force unit—has been respected in every following century of EM time. Our present 30th-century models include the four original basic categories, plus the next three log multiples. The largest vessel in our commerce today is the tremendous Megaton Transport, which is an exact 10^3 multiple, in all of its design characteristics, of the pioneer 1,000-ton Heavy Transport model. And Megaton's one million ton gross weight finds itself propelled by an adequate and reliable 1.01 GeeForce P.M.I. Propulsion system.

But already we have leaped 10 centuries past Plum Brook, Ohio, and the historic convention. It is best that we check our course, to keep the story of P.M.I. Propulsion in proper chronology. For, in a complete analysis, there is more to this most fascinating of the EM Technologies than "mere hardware"; and the paths that led out from Plum Brook carried much of the initial life-blood to our Culture and Age. Our total appreciation for the beginning of P.M.I. Propulsion, and of EM Science itself can be enriched by returning into history and participating, at least vicariously, in that era-genetic gathering of the 300 scientists in A.D. 1985.

WILLIAM JOSEPHS

Guest of honor at the NASA's Plum Brook assembly was William Josephs, the Discoverer of EM Science. His personal appearance at the presentation of P.M.I. Propulsion was considered by America's senior scientists to be a guarantee of P.M.I.'s feasibility as a working EM Technology. Almost overnight, since the February 25 announcement of the incredible Scientific Breakthrough, the humble Discoverer of EM Rayforms had become world famous. But to all of his colleagues who had worked side by side with him during the long 30 years of EM research, Josephs had always been held in the highest professional and personal esteem. It was William Josephs' dual genius, as a man of Science and as a man concerned for all mankind, that so spontaneously and forcefully impressed on America's policy-making Science Advisory Council the realization that the EM Discoveries held a promise of fabulous and boundless benefits for the people of all the nations on Earth. Josephs' magnanimous proposal for worldwide endowment of the technological wonders of the new Science won immediate endorsement from the enthusiastic Council; and out of the EM Discovery disclosure sessions came the United States of America's daring plan to raise the hopes of the world via the EM Technologies. P.M.I. Propulsion was to play an important part in this program, for it was to be one of the three EM Technologies selected by the President's Advisory Council to undergo development at maximum national effort. The three—P.M.I. Propulsion, Weather and Climate Control, and Elemental Separation—were scheduled for operational demonstration to the world nations in A.D. 2000.

But total confidence and approbation of the new Science was not automatic. The public announcement of the EM Discoveries preceeded Plum Brook by only two months. Most of the learned men and women in attendance had barely looked into the details of EM Science; for actually, very little specific technical information had been released by the American guardians of the Discoveries. In the mixed atmosphere of excitement and perplexity over the sensational prospects for the new EM Technologies, there were many informed citizens, including those in scientific exposures, who had apprehensions and misgivings. Inwardly, people from all walks of life must have been searching their minds and memories for re-assurance. And openly, they were asking one another: "Hadn't most of man's inventions and the derivatives of scientific knowledge in recent years—yes, in recent centuries—been directed and confined to military technology? Just what kind of a dream is this P.M.I. Propulsion? And what in principle, in common plausible terms, are these EM Discoveries that can beget such fantastic technologies? Is there sound basis for their backing by the American Government? If it turns out that these proposed technologies are technically sound, do we risk economic and industrial chaos by converting to them? What is to become of our jet and rocket techniques, of conventional internal combustion engines, of automobiles and highways themselves, of present electrical power generation plants and their vast distribution systems— all representing billions of dollars of investment? Can it be true, as suggested by the American President's Science Advisory Council, that the EM Discoveries will revolutionize basic industrial processes by utilizing Elemental Separation Technologies to synthesize iron, steel, and hundreds of other chemical compounds? And what is this gross absurdity of man controlling the weather and competing with Nature to build new climatic zones over the face of the Earth?

"On the plus side, we do know that the Government of the United States has made the announcement of the Discoveries. And we know that some of the finest men of science have devoted their lives to this EM research. Yes, and many respected scientific minds have already endorsed the accuracy of Josephs' report, and the potential feasibility of the EM Technologies. But still, will we be asked to accept blindly, without favor of understanding, new aspects of Nature that exceed the limits of human comprehension? Indeed, some of William Josephs' substance of light and electricity, EM Rayform, and magnetic attribute relationships may be beyond the limit of understanding of even the most capable scientific intellects of our 20th century."

In the select company at Plum Brook, however, these normal human apprehensions for the unknown and the strange were less in evidence, or at least, under control. Here, in the main, were men and women accustomed to the uncertainty, and to the patience and perservance of scientific research. And was there ever a scientist who was not captivated by the dream of participating in the bonanza of a Natural Revelation? As the delegates awaited the guest of honor, there was an obvious air of pride surrounding them, pride in this major breakthrough for science, and in their own good fortune to be invited to share in the rewards that had come to Josephs and his EM research team.

ADDRESS AT PLUM BROOK BY WILLIAM JOSEPHS—
A.D. 1985

"Ladies and gentlemen, my respected colleagues, members of the World Scientific Body: I am deeply honored to be with you on this beautiful Spring day. It is a humbling feeling that I have, to celebrate a great time in our lives, a birthday in history, with so brilliant and so accomplished a body of men and women from every sector of our planet. At the outset, I must confide to you that I cannot suppose to stand before you as the proposer of a new Age for Science, as the annunciator of an unbelievably bountiful era for mankind throughout the world, without acknowledging an innermost feeling that our efforts and activities over the past 30 years of research into the phenomenon of Light and Electricity have been guided by a far greater force than ourselves. So many of my partners in EM research, Doctors Ballard and Herald, Doctor Karwoski and others share with me this deep sense of Providential direction. Some of us have the real impression that it is, truly, a supervision from above. I do not say this to startle you, nor to invoke a holiness onto our purpose. It is for each man, according to his innermost substance, either to acknowledge or to turn away from his own convictions of human purpose and Providential plan. But, sooner or later in our days and toils, we all come to know that every facet of our lives has its ordered time and place. And we must keep ourselves ready in mind and body so that we may participate with ebullient effort in each new opportunity—scientific or otherwise—as we seek understanding of the fundamental "whys" and "hows" about us. For now, as we begin our first open assembly on EM Science and Technology, let us duly pay respect to the privilege that we of the EM research group feel for our part in His Plan.

Newton's Laws of Motion, translated into everyday economics, tell us that nothing in life is free or without cost. Thus, by your presence here today, each man and woman, expertly capable in his or her branch of Science, assumes a share in our new responsibility. For here today, we must adjudge the merits, the hazards, the purpose, and the Plan associated with the new knowledge that will now become a part of us. The decision of this eminent Scientific College, herein gathered, to utilize the EM Discoveries either for mankind, or for the destruction of mankind, rests upon the freedom of choice that each member of this body possesses. The fate or the future of our perplexed world depends upon your wisdom.

As you know, the EM Science Research Team has recently presented to the American Presidential Science Advisory Council our report entitled: *The EM Scientific Discoveries*. This paper, in summation of man's newest increment of knowledge in the Natural Sciences, represents 30 years of inspired investigations that penetrated deeply into the Physical Nature. But we hardly started from zero; and in this sense, the EM Discoveries are a continuation of the technical knowledge that men of science have painstakingly accumulated during all of history. Without the heritage entrusted to us by Isaac Newton, by Maxwell, Gilbert, Huygens, Robert Boyle, by Faraday, Hertz and Marconi, by Oersted, Neils Bohr, Albert Einstein, Landau, Planck, Michelson, Fermi, Oppenheimer, Doyle, and Walker—and including large and small contributions even from many members in this assembly room—without these pioneers of science, we could never have come to our success. In the longer view, EM Research is no more than an extension of man's eternal quest for knowledge, initiated in ancient Greece by Thales, Anaximander, Pythagoras, Paramenades, and Archimedes. Our breakthrough today, in the late 20th century, into the EM Chapter of Science is based upon solid foundations, more than 2,000 years in construction.

Our particular subject here at the NASA's Plum Brook Laboratory is P.M.I. Propulsion. This fabulous offshoot of the EM Discoveries could command our total interest. However, I am sure there are some of us who would like to hear about the parent of the many promising technologies that will absorb our attentions in the coming years. That parent, of course, is EM Science. Let me tell you briefly how it started, what it is, what some of its Rayform classifications can do, and what the future holds, if we dare to guess. The name *EM* affixed itself quite spontaneously to our early work, which centered around Electro-Magnetic theories. Although the letters *E* and *M* may also suggest the wonders of the Energy-Mass relationship developed and explained by Albert Einstein, they were not initially so intended. Just in case we were asked, our research group has put together one of those super-concise definitions, which in turn, requires re-defininition of its own words. If not at this moment, perhaps later on you will agree to the form of its statement. *EM Science, we say, is that knowledge of the attribute-carrying Rayforms that gives man the capability to determine and to control the Status of Universal Materia.* Now, having given you that explanation of *EM,* which quite possibly still leaves you searching, allow me to tell you, as further background, something of our work.

Thirty years ago, in 1955, a small group of dedicated scientists and engineers, with university and industrial affiliations in the American Midwest, entered into a serious discussion, a critical analysis—or at any rate, an honest assessment of 20th-century technology. Our small group was agreed, in preamble, on two points of order. These two subjective guidelines became the underlying theme, the common return ground, for our scientific discussions. The *first point* was an accusation that modern technologies had wantonly exploited scientific knowledge. The accusation contended that the products of our technologies had become the dominating interest of scientific minds to the exclusion of a continuing ardent search for the fundamental scientific basis of each technology, that, in fact, many modern technologies were operating without positive scientific explanation.

The *second point,* not quite as self-critical as the first, noted that scientific evidence and observation continues to add credibility to the ancient Theory of Oneness—the amazing interlocking relationship between the forms of Nature that we call mass, energy, gravity, motion, light, time, and space. We asked ourselves: Is there somewhere a common denominator acceptable to all the forms of Nature, one that governs and permits their remarkable circumstantial and conditional interchangeability? These two points in preamble to the discussions of a group of ex-college boys and industrial technicians may seem overly profound, but they are indicative of our serious and sincere interest in the state of Science.

With regard to point one, we note that today we live in a technological environment, whose facilities are founded upon natural phenomena adjusted by human invention. But the basic substance of many of these phenomena remains a mystery. In our technological affluence we revel in the comfort and convenience afforded to our lives by Electricity, by Nuclear Energy, by Radiowave Propagation—all of which defy total and positive scientific explanation. We know how to use them; but we truly cannot explain their basic constitution. And we also take for granted the natural wonders of Light and Sunshine, of Magnetism and Ionization, of the inexplicable process of Photosynthesis wherein sunlight converts carbon dioxide into plant sugar, the basic fuel of life. We have even forgotten to marvel at the miracle of the human mind and body, and at the beauty and stability of our Earth in the vastness of the Universe. As our young team started out on this adventure, we seriously questioned: Is this preoccupation with our material achievements, this complacency and disinterest in basic scientific explanation, serving the progress of mankind? We liked to think that our telling cast of self-indictment, as well as our condemnation of the general non-scientific attitudes, would provoke us toward a renewed pursuit of basic scientific knowledge.

As a further prod to pull us out of our satisfied resignments and to push us into constructive research, we reminded ourselves, via point number two, that for years we have lived under the sledgehammer-like hint that all of the elements that constitute our Natural Universe are uniquely similar in the style of their atomic formation. Perhaps, we counseled ourselves, we are no closer to this mystery of Nature than were Thales and Anaxamander who, in 600 B.C., sensed the same possibility that all material composition had a common origin. Yet, in a modern, contemporary assessment we asked: Are we not on a plateau as was Maxwell, who in 1870 with Faraday's first principles of Electricity as his sledgehammer hint, predicted the existence of electromagnetic waves? In the middle of the 20th century, we have been daily witnesses to the marvel of nuclear release, to the drama of elemental transmutation played by the radioactive isotopes, and to the intriguing development of plasma electricity. Can it be, in our time, at our accelerated rate of tapping Nature's secrets, that we shall discover the link that binds all matter, motion, and time?

Within the first year of our organization, thanks to the sponsorship of several farsighted corporate industries—whose directors shared our purposes and discontents—we found ourselves engaged in full-time research into basic electro-magnetic physics. It became our exciting fortune early in the following year, 1956, when we isolated a phenomenal system within, but apparently independent of the electro-magnetic spectrum. Because groups in this new physical system resembled typical electric and magnetic wave forms, and often possessed the characteristics of ordinary light rays, we called them, the EM Rayforms. The startling definitive capability of these Rayforms was their apparent function in establishing and controlling the physical state of materials. The EM Rayforms, it seemed, acted as carriers of the various and multitudinous physical attributes that define materials.

The initial detection of the Rayform carrier phenomenon came while we were working with ordinary yellow sulfur that had been placed under cryogenic or near-absolute-zero temperature condition. We found that the magnetic properties—intensity and opposite-object selectivity—of cryogenically conditioned sulfur could be induced by "synthetic" signals that we applied, or modulated, on top of a low-frequency electrical field surrounding the sulfur. Unknown to us at the time was the circumstantial existence of EM Rayform 36; its spontaneous constitution favored by the severe cryogenic ambient. Rayform 36 was the real carrier of our signals. Its presence was confirmed by the persistence our applied signals for a full second of time after the low frequency electrical field had collapsed to zero. Only the existence of an entirely independent carrier could account for our observation.

Following the cryogenic sulfur findings, we extended our investigations into other materials, and under additional extreme temperature, pressure, and impact-velocity ambients. We were elated to discover a similiar presence, under these uncommon physical circumstances, of several other Rayforms. From these Rayforms, we eventually were able to separate, or demodulate, a series of conventional electromagnetic signals. The signals that ride on the EM Rayform carriers, we believe, can run the full range of the electromagnetic spectrum—from the long almost-immeasurable electric wave all the way down to the very short X and Gamma-Ray wavelengths. At the present stage of our investigations, however, we have had our best results detecting signals with wavelengths between the ultra shortwave Radio and the Visual Light. This is the range of wavelengths from 1 meter (10^{10} Angstrom units) down to the 3800 Angstrom of violet light.

But the significant feature about all of these signals that attach themselves to the various Rayform carriers is that they—the signals—are proportional and mathematically analogous to many of the conventional physical parameters. This is to say, we have found these signals to represent—if not, in fact, to be—the physical attributes we know as temperature, pressure, color, hardness, solubility, magnetic intensity and selectivity, and the multitude of other static environmental coordinates that characterize a material. During the exciting months in the late 1950s and early 1960s (A.D. 1950 and A.D. 1960), we discovered the existence, on still other Rayform carriers, of signals that we correlated to the dynamics of velocity, acceleration, force, energy flow rate (power), gravity effect, and, if you can believe it, to the geometrical effects on material of motion, space, and time.

With each new Rayform finding, as you can imagine, our enthusiasm and respect for EM Science grew; for we realized that our privileged team was, each day, further opening the secret book of Nature. And our new knowledge, we suspected, could give to man an almost incredible control over the state and geometry of material matter. In our "New World" of EM Rayforms we began to refer to materials as having *status,* which we defined as "the combined total of the physical attributes of a material under a set of specific circumstantial conditions." We stipulated that these attributes and circumstantial conditions—

within the definition of *status*—must be viewed not in a local reference but in a relativity to the universal environment.

Our earthly understanding of Nature's materials has always been confined within narrow, comfortable ambients. Human forms and beings that we are, our survival instincts compel us to select life-supportive environmental conditions. It is humanly natural that we should understand Nature's materials in a sense and proportion related to human life. In the immensity of the Universe, however, the range of physical conditions extends extremely above and below that of our human adaptation. To match this universal range of physical circumstances, there is a corresponding range in the *status* of every material. This broad variation of *status* suggests another expansion of our vocabulary, substituting the more inclusive *materia* for the ordinary material, which by custom has come to imply only visible and tangible substances. Within the full range of environmental circumstances and condition, *materia,* then, can be a substance composed of mass, energy, or the radiation forms of energy—or, it can be a complex combination of all of these.

Our 30 years of introduction to EM Science have led us to believe—and the evidence is positive and conclusive—that the transfers, in Nature, of physical attributes onto *materia* are conveyed via the Rayform carriers. Our knowledge of these carriers or ties between *materia* and the environment of the *materia*—viewed within the context of universal relativity—constitutes, and is, EM Science. The Rayforms of EM Science have been with us—or shall we say, at work in the universe—since the beginning of time. Several Rayforms have even been very close to all of us; although we have never identified them as members of the EM family. It has been our scientific rationale to look upon many types of electromagnetic radiation, from electricity and radio, through light, to gamma and cosmic rays as being in themselves final forms representing electro-magnetic and electrostatic strains of space. Now, we offer evidence to show these common wave phenomena are merely a few of the many "signal-burdens" carried by EM Rayforms. Yet, the carrier and its burden are so similar in many of our acquaintances—such as common electricity—

that it does no harm, for ordinary purposes, to think of them as one and the same. Indeed, the carriers are often called electromagnetic Rayforms, because they appear to share many of the attributes of members of the electromagnetic spectrum. However, we must emphasize that EM Rayforms are a separate family within Nature and are not totally equatable with electromagnetic waves. Rayforms are best understood as not being, in themselves, a conditioning influence or a substantive physical controller of the *status* of *materia,* but solely as being the carrier that conveys the influence, in either direction, between *materia* and the environment. Although we may like to think of Rayforms and electromagnetic waves as cousins, there is one amazing characteristic of Rayforms that confirms that the two cannot be considered equal and identical entities in Nature. This characteristic came to our attention during research into Rayform propagation rates.

All electromagnetic waves exhibit the singular and limiting maximum velocity in space of 3×10^{10} centimeters per second, or in British-American units, 186,000 miles per second—the common velocity of light. And many EM Rayforms also operate at this same propagation rate. But there is substantial evidence to indicate that a few of the 100 known Rayforms are capable of breaking this so-called light barrier. These remarkable few, according to our calculations, should be able to operate at positive (and also at the negative or reciprocal) harmonic multiples of 2, 3, 5, and 7 times their nominal or light velocity. We have yet much to learn about this predictable release from the time-honored speed limit posted by Nature. Quite possibly the remarkable property of multiple and fractional light velocities may some-day turn out to be the most significant of the EM Discoveries. At present levels, however, it remains the most mysterious. Yet, this sliver of EM knowledge prompts a speculation for the eventual feasibility of inter-stellar or even inter-galactic space travel during a man's short term under the stars. However, we know so little at this state and stage of EM Science, and it does not seem that in our era, of for at least several generations, that we shall be capable of utilizing to mankind's advantage this portentous knowledge of multiple light velocities. I tell you of this still closely held secret of Nature—shall we say—for purely academic reasons, but with the reminder that the book of Nature is endless. There will be many more piece-by-piece solutions to come out of this awesome guidebook of Creation, some of them more profound than even our EM Discoveries. These future concessions by Nature will certainly be the rewards for scientific research by generations yet to come.

There is always this temptation to dream and to get lost in the future of EM Science. But there is also the sensational reality of our Discoveries to date; and there is much work to do in getting them off to a good start. So let us stay within our own time. Perhaps now, you are prepared to hear some specific reports about the better known members of the Rayform family, and something about their possible assignments in EM technologies. Later in our session we will get down to our principal topic and business of the day: the Technology of P.M.I. Propulsion. Therein we will call upon your very best resources of imagination and scientific confidence.

The first observed EM Rayform, discovered in association with the cryogenic magnetic sulfur program in 1956, put us on a fast track to the rest of the family. During the following 29 years, our team of EM pioneers has been successful in confirming 100 different and distinct Rayform identities. It has often been said in a generalization that "Science is our knowledge of the Order of the Universe." In a classic, though not unexpected obedience to this definition, the 100 members of the EM Rayform family have, so far, aligned themselves in quite orderly fashion into a Periodic Table of Rayforms, tantalizingly similar to the well-known Periodic Table of the Elements. It may be of interest to you if we glance briefly through this Periodic Table of the EM Rayforms and talk about those that appear to offer the greatest potential for application in our present and future technologies. You will notice, as we have mentioned previously, that many of these Rayforms have been with us for years as friends and partners, using their electromagnetic names. For instance, Rayform 10 is synonymous with our common everyday electricity, which is carried on this Rayform. Incidentally, Rayform 10 retains its #10 designation in EM classification whether the electricity it carries is A.C. or D.C. In an EM sense, A.C. and

D.C. modes are minor oscillatory or wave type variations, all of which are acceptable passengers on Rayform #10.

Another most interesting servant of man is Rayform 27. Heat energy, the same that warms our coffee, burns our toast, and comes in such large portions from the Sun, is conveyed as infrared radiations by EM Rayform 27. In EM terminology, the processes of applying and removing infrared energy are called Adsorption and Desorption, and there is great confidence in our ability to manage Rayform 27 in these operations. We have given many years of study and investigation to this particular Rayform, because it lends itself so readily to controlled technology and offers great promise of becoming our most bounteous benefactor. In addition to our technical capability to control the amount of Adsorption and Desorption of infrared energy onto Rayform 27, we have the opportunity for a major breakthrough in electric power distribution via Rayform 27. For more than 10 years, an EM Research divisional team has been perfecting a dual transformation technique wherein Rayform 27, with an infrared burden, is stepped directly down to Rayform 10, common electricity. Our electrical power companies will soon feel the economic impact of this development. But an orderly changeover to an R 27 wireless-power economy would require at least 20 years to completion once the Rayform Power Technology achieves equipment design approval.

So great is our confidence for a successful technological management of heat-energy Adsorption and Desorption on Rayform 27 that the EM Research team has designed and proposed a system—on a rather grand scale enclosing an area of 100 square miles—of Sunshine control. As you may have anticipated, from recent newspaper accounts, this proposed harnessing of the tremendous power in Sunshine will be part of an over-all program to control the weather in specific geographical locations. Within the coming years we will all hear more and more about the role of EM Science in Weather Control. I mention this project now, to point out the expectations we hold for its scientific keystone, Rayform 27—the carrier of infrared energy.

Two close allies of Rayform 27 are next in series in the Periodic Table. EM Rayform 28 carries electromagnetic waves associated with visible light, which of course, range from the reds at 7600 Angstrom to the violets at 3800 Angstrom units of wavelength. Ultraviolet radiations travel on carrier Rayform #29. These three: 27, 28, and 29, for obvious reasons, are called the Sunshine group. However, there are a host of other Rayforms that find employment on the route between the Sun and Planet Earth. Numbers 76 and 77 pack the × radiations; and the entire "80" series (80 thru 89) of these tireless freight carriers handle the tens of thousands of different gamma and cosmic rays.

Magnetic Number influences are carried by the "30" group of Rayforms. Conventional magnetism, associated with iron—and the property that makes our compasses seek the North Pole—is hooked up with Rayform 38. But there are literally thousands of additional magnetic and paramagnetic attributes that regulate the *status* of *materia*. And most of these are carried by the various orders, or exponential multiples, of the "30" series magnetic-attribute carriers. In and by itself, the "30" group of Rayforms will open up a field of unlimited technological opportunity. By utilizing Rayforms of this magnetic series in Elemental Separation techniques, we have been able to extract selected elemental components from aqueous solutions—and again, in quantities of massive proportion. You will become well acquainted with the "30" series of Rayforms within the next decade, for this group of 10 from the Periodic Table of Rayforms is to be the EM scientific foundation for several large-scale Elemental Separation installations that will soon go on stream to treat millions of acre-feet of water every day.

It is so easy to become totally wrapped up in the excitement of EM Science. I could continue for hours—if your patience and taxed imaginations could stand the ordeal—telling you about Rayform 17, the water vapor carrier; about R 47 and R 48, the radio wave propagation carriers; about R 72, the viscosity attribute carrier; and R 74, the hardness characteristic carrier. But there are not hours enough in our present convention to cover all of these prodigious subjects. So far, in this introductory, I have spoken only about the successes of our EM Research team. I assure you that there also have been many roads in our experience that have led us up blind alleys. Out of the abundance of scientific data covering the full field of 100 Rayforms, we must admit that we can tell you no more than a presumed name and a predicted position in the Periodic Table for 25 of the Rayforms. In addition to this failure to expand on these mysterious 25, we have been able to control attributive modulations on only 51 of the 75 positively known Rayforms. Occasionally we remind ourselves—in an effort to keep our feet on solid ground, and our heads out of the clouds —that we have only scratched the surface in our quest for understanding of the EM facet of Nature. We are grateful, of course, for our partial successes. Our level of knowledge in the present 51 "cooperating" Rayforms has given us full confidence to effect substantial adjustments in the *status* of many *materiae*. Yet, 49 of the EM Rayforms have turned us back completely in their totally successful blockade of our efforts to bridle and harness them. We know that they are there, but their secrets—the knowledge of the attributes they carry—belong to future generations.

I know that what I have accounted to you thus far may have left you short of breath, or at least somewhat incredulous. New knowledge in such strideful amounts strains the mind for acceptance. These are truly amazing breakthroughs in Science, and even the relatively few facts that I have related this morning will take time for mental digestion. Do not feel that you are alone in this intellectual absorption problem. With every grant of new knowledge that has come to the EM Science team, there has always been the human task; yes, the challenge, to digest it, to marvel at its potential, and to reassure ourselves that, indeed, we are not dealing in fantasies. It has taken our dedicated team all of these 30 years to consider the wonder, let alone the technical details, of the Discoveries. As we are all of the same basic human substance, take reassurance then, that for each man and woman of our distinguished assembly today, it will certainly take a while between the hearing and the believing of EM Science."

P.M.I. PROPULSION
—a continuation, adapted from the address by William Josephs at Plum Brook, Ohio, A.D. 1985

"With the foregoing brief discussion of the Rayforms hopefully serving as an introduction to EM Science, let us move directly into P.M.I. Propulsion. Prepare yourselves for a remarkable scientific adventure. Receive and hear it today at Plum Brook with patience and an effort for approbation, and, in a few years, become participating pilots and passengers in this dynamic EM Technology. Do not allow my several previous allusions to P. M.I.'s credibility to alarm you. P.M.I. Propulsion is a scientifically sound reality. It has been field-tested and proven, albeit on a small, but still, a confirmatory scale. In acquiring an understanding of this revolutionary propulsion system—and this is the only caution that we advise—you may want to condition your own minds to view and to accept the EM Scientific fundamentals of P.M.I. within the context of universal relativity. For it is only in this sphere that the Projected Magnetic Image *materia* assumes its unique *status*. And it is by virtue of this universal *status* of the Image *materia* that we are able to effect a transfer of energy and to adapt this energy to aerospace-vessel propulsion.

Before we directly tackle the P.M.I. hardware in a prototype aerospace vessel, two general equipment considerations should be noted:

Most Rayforms do not originate or persist spontaneously in our earthly environment. Therefore, EM technological processes, including P.M.I. Propulsion, require a C-M-A (Converter-Magnetizer-Accelerator) to constitute the specific Rayforms that serve each technology. The C-M-A is, of course, at the core of the EM Discoveries; for it is the basic "chamber of ambients"—the cryogenic temperature regulator, the super-magnetizer, and the Lach 1.01 (light velocity of 1.01) particle accelerator—in which Rayforms are established. The usual source *materia* used in C-M-A's is Rayform 10, common D.C. electric current, which lends itself to the conversion and constitution of other Rayforms under the "universal" ambients within the C-M-A. Attributes, or burden-signals, which the Rayforms carry are modulated onto Rayform carriers in a C-M-A contiguous section—which we sometimes lightly call the grocery department. Its technical name is the A. & P.P. Unit, or Adsorption and Pulse Projection Unit. The A. & P.P. Unit gathers freshly constituted Rayforms from the C-M-A, adsorbs attributive signals onto them, and projects the loaded carriers in controlled pulses toward a target. Rayform pulses leaving the A. & P.P. Unit usually travel at the speed of light, 186,000 miles per second. Every aerospace vessel in our program will be equipped with an on-board C-M-A, and a smaller emergency C-M-A. Three specially designed A. & P.P. Units tailored to the Rayform requirements of P.M.I. Propulsion will also be included in the on-board equipment.

The second preliminary consideration concerns the primary fuel source to be used for generating the Image substance. In this regard we have—theoretically—an unlimited choice. But, practically, we are looking for as dense and substantial a material as we can find, which can adsorb directly and efficiently onto a Rayform carrier and can also assume a high degree of magnetic density. Thus, we would not want to select any of the electromagnetic forms of light or even a radio frequency burden, since these have almost insignificant substantive density. We might think of choosing water vapor as our fuel, since it can adsorb directly onto Rayform 17, and it certainly has adequate substantive density. But unfortunately, we find it difficult to control the transition of water vapor into a *status* with sufficient magnetic density. The only other directly adsorbable materials that we know of, at this time in the Science, are Hydrogen and Helium, which can both be adsorbed onto Rayform 18, and Fluorine and Chlorine, which adsorb onto Rayform 19. Perhaps someday in later refinements of the Technology, Hydrogen and Helium may be adapted to P.M.I. Image fueling, but in our time there is the restriction of their minimal substantive densities and of their comparatively low levels of ultimate magnetic density. And so, by critical comparison of all the possible fuel sources, we have selected ordinary Chlorine as the most advantageous material for our Projected Image. Chlorine has sufficient density, both substantively and in the magnetic sense. It offers good reliability in the direct adsorption and desorption processes. Incidentally, on-board fuel weight has no bearing on this selection. In fact, even the largest vessels that we contemplate will be built with no more than 100 kilo (220 pounds avoirdupois) original fuel supply. It is expected that this quantity will provide image-substance *materia* for 10 years of operation at nominal GeeForce and energy consumption levels.

Now, to the specific P.M.I. hardware associated with the task of propelling our aerospace vessel. The on-board equipment consists of three principal groups. Each group and its particular Rayforms carry the functional responsibility for a stage of the propulsion system. These three stages are as follows: Projection, Transition, and Attraction.

In the Projection stage, Rayform 19 pulses are utilized to carry adsorbed Chlorine from the Projection A. & P.P. Unit to the Image "screen," located at a controlled distance ahead of the vessel. On the screen, let's say at the nominal projection distance of 1 micro-second (1,116 feet) used in the proposed 1,000-Ton Heavy Transport, the conveyed fuel substance is instantaneously (within 1 nano-second or 1.116 feet) desorbed and held in projection on the screen, to become the Primary Image.

The Transition-stage equipment now enters to perform its astonishing function. Two EM Rayforms are combinely employed in the complex Transition process. Rayform 9, the universal density carrier, plays the major role in the Transition; with Rayform 37^3, the third-order magnetic number carrier of Chlorine, seeming to serve the process as an environmental catalyst. Rayform 9 and Rayform 37^3 are multidyned—that is, they are multiplied one by the other—and their product is focused onto the Primary Image at its projected spot ahead of the aerospace vessel. At a controlled rate, the Primary Image now undergoes a change or Transition in its nature that is perhaps the most astounding maneuver in EM Science. The substantive mass of the Primary Image, adjusted to a constant accumulation of less than one-half pound, is transposed into a *materia* with tremendous relative magnetic density. The new *materia* assumes a *status* physically classified as *Neutron Density*. In the case of our Heavy Transport aerospace vessel, this Transition or Secondary Image has a calculated relative magnetic mass of 2×10^{13} tons. The only comparison with this incomprehensible action and consequent density is in Nature's formation of the Neutron and White Dwarf Stars in the deep celestial abyss. But remember, our ponderous Secondary Image is a child of Universal Relativity. In this regard, the particular influence of Rayform 37^3 in the Transition stage is important to comprehend, since the Magnetic Number influence of R 37^3 establishes the Secondary Image's *first degree of relativity*.

Possibly you have sensed the physical circumstances that now prevail, at least in relativity, and can appreciate the potential Force of Universal Gravitation that exists between the 1,000-ton aerospace vessel and the 2×10^{13} ton Secondary or Neutron Image. And to complete the circuit, to hook onto this fantastic mass out in front of our vessel, the final stage of P.M.I. Propulsion hardware comes into action. In this, the Attraction stage, once again two Rayforms, R 57 and R 37 in its 5th order, share the task of harnessing the Image to the vessel. Rayform 57 is one of the sturdy family of Force-carrying Rayforms. It has the capacity to convey the attributes of attraction between bodies of concentrated mass. Forces of attraction flow on Rayform #57 in complete accordance with Newton's Physical Law of Universal Gravitation. As you well know, Newton's honored Gravitation Precept states that particles of matter—throughout the Universe —attract each other with a force directly proportional to the product of their masses and inversely proportional to the square of the distance between them.

The P.M.I. Attraction stage further multiplies the natural mass-attraction phenomenon by utilizing Rayform 37, in its 5th exponential order, to provide a highly permeable, concentrated path for the lines of force that link the Secondary Image and the aerospace vessel. As an additional, more subtle function, Rayform 37^5 in the Attraction stage, pairs up with its cousin the 3rd order of Rayform 37 used in the prior Transition stage, to establish a *second degree of relativity*. Thus, there exists between the initial and final stages—between the Projection platform and the Attraction stage drawplate—a double-magnetic or super relativity. This special case of relativity enables the Attraction force vectors in our propulsion system to apply a net positive 1.01 GeeForce to the 1,000-ton Heavy Transport and to pull it free and clear of Earth's gravity on its way into the boundless heavens. In an hour's time from lift-off, at its moderate but constant and continuous 1.01 g. acceleration, our prototype will reach the 350-mile altitude level. From there it will continue to increase its velocity by more than 700 miles per hour (initially, and at a much greater rate as Earth gravity diminishes) during each hour of a voyage of almost unlimited durational possibility.

And there, in the briefest fundamental terms, is P.M.I. Propulsion. But I see some upraised eyebrows among our calculating and learned audience. Obviously, you are concerned, that if our P.M.I.-propelled Heavy Transport is indeed aloft, it is there in contradiction to Sir Isaac Newton's Third Law of Motion. Let me reassure you that Sir Isaac's inviolable law of reactions—that every action has its equal and opposite reaction—has not left us, and is just as valid as it ever was. Your awareness of this guiding principle of Mechanics is, in fact, equal to our EM Research team's concern for kinetic accuracy. A true and effective solution of the action-reaction force equation has been a basic design premise in the development of this dynamic technology. We can verify that there is a net positive reaction on our aerospace vessel by viewing it—or if you prefer, by placing the vessel—in a position where it can take mechanical advantage of the double relativity existing between itself and the Primary and Secondary Images. Allow me to illustrate this vital circumstance in specific terms:

We have shown that the Projection stage A. & P.P. Unit sends out a measurable amount of Chlorine via direct adsorption onto Rayform 19. The substance of this fuel *materia* amounts to no more than one-half pound and is projected into the Image screen space at the velocity of light. The Chlorine flow requires about a full second to fill or accumulate this load into the screen. There is no need for a more rapid deposition, because once the nominal substantive mass is in place, only a sustaining or holding action is necessary to maintain the Image. Incidentally, there is virtually no consumption of the Image substance, and at trips-end during Propulsion System shutdown, the Image *materia* returns to the on-board Chlorine storage bunker. The point of this explanation is to show that while, theoretically, there is a force in reaction to the Image projection-sustaining effort, it is minimal and absolutely insignificant to the task of moving the 1,000-ton aerospace vessel. However, this minimal reactive force has a technological and real-propulsion significance. It represents the total reaction force of *both* the Primary and Secondary Images. And therein lies the enabling wonder of P.M.I. Propulsion, a wonder that would be preposterous outside the realm of EM Science.

For real-propulsion purposes, we view the total Image re-action force in a direct proportion to the 8-ounce Primary, and not to the 2×10^{13} ton relative magnetic mass of the Secondary Image—whose *status* is a function in universal relativity. The attractive force pulling the 1,000-ton vessel toward the 2×10^{13} (20 mega-mega) ton relative magnetic mass is, therefore—by Primary Image reference—virtually unopposed. And the Images are held in Projection, against this huge attractive force, by not much more than the force of a light beam.

Obviously then, the resolution of Newton's Third Law of Motion—calling for an algebraically satisfactory cancellation of forces between the two masses—must take place in a medium that is independent of our aerospace vessel. And in our scene, this can only be within the sphere of universal relativity in the Transition stage. It may help if we view events in the Transition stage—the conversion of one-half pound of Primary Image to a Secondary *materia* characterized by a neutron-like magnetic mass —as being a sidewise action and reaction, or an event in universal relativity not related, in either quantitative size or direction, to the realistic vector of propulsion force.

Undoubtedly, the Transition stage of P.M.I. Propulsion dup-licates in some still uncertain manner—although on an extremely small scale—the process that Nature carries out in the continual evolution of the billions of stars in the deep heavens. We suspect that MASS—ENERGY—and GRAVITY are all involved in this incredible interchange of *status* as stars explode into supernovae and then recondense into dense white-dwarf and neutron Pulsars. But more and more, with each new day in EM Science, we feel sure that these materiae, MASS—ENERGY—GRAVITY and perhaps even others involved in the colossity of stellar evolution, are of one and the same substance. The Image *materia* in the P.M.I. Transition stage, we must similiarly conclude, is of this same character. Mathematical documentation of Primary and Secondary Image behavior in the kinetics of P.M.I. Propulsion bears out this judgment.

We should point out, admittedly and with a share of disappointment, that in this early period of EM Science it is not yet clear to us *how* the Rayforms R 9 and R 37[3] manage the Transition of a half pound of Chlorine into the tremendous energy equivalent that is represented in the Secondary Image. We can only say that the Secondary Image is a form of magnetic mass, and/or Gravitational Inertial Energy, available only to a relative attractor. And to other unrelated objects it is nothing, has no equality or inequality, and not even any reference; for perhaps, outside of the sphere of universal relativity, it does not exist.

On the affirmative and realistic side of the Technology, however, our P.M.I. attractive-force test data are reasonable and tangible, and mathematically sound. Even though we lack a total scientific insight into the nature of the Transition stage, we cannot reject these real findings and technical documentations. And it does no harm to the concept of our new Science, nor will it conflict with the reality of our recently successful P.M.I. test flights, to visualize the Primary and Secondary Images out in front of us, moving along on course with us, as if they were a fixed extension of our vessel. They—the Images—have immense analytical value.

Well, our doubts almost got the best of us; but now again, we have the Images back with us. And let us hope, in their correct perspective. Out of scientific curiosity—in continuation—we might ask: Just what appearance do these "analytic" Images assume; that is, from the viewpoint of an observer standing on the Attraction deck of our aerospace vessel? Some of our more imaginative experts from the EM P.M.I. team, in fact, have ventured an answer to this curiosity; and their description is based upon actual GeeForce readings taken from our test mock-ups. We must bear in mind, however, that the picture our venturesome experts draw for us is strictly a mathematical analogy, because I am sure that none of them have physically seen the Images—at least not during working hours.

The Primary Image configuration, they tell us, is more or less nebulous. They give or take that it occupies a volume of about one cubic foot and consists of several billion Chlorine molecules orbiting in a donut-shaped racecourse no more than 1.116 feet (one nano-second) in its major diameter. This shape and internal activity, it seems, would favor the Primary's tendency toward Transition. Now, the Secondary Image is more predictable, and the mathematicians in the group find great joy in painting its portrait. The suspected shape and mass characteristics of this huge fellow are derived from two well-known mechanical force equations; and from a correlation to our present knowledge of the celestial Pulsars.

Specifically—and to get down to their terms—the two force equations tell us that the mutual attraction, in dynes of force, between the Secondary Image and the Attraction stage drawplate is equal to $G \dfrac{M_1 M_2}{r_2}$, and also to $K \dfrac{Q_1 Q_2}{r_2}$. The first equation,

$$F = G \frac{M_1 M_2}{r_2}$$

, of course, is Newton's honored Law of Universal Gravity, with G representing the gravitational constant $6.66 \times 10^{-8} \dfrac{dyne\ cm^2}{gm^2}$. M_1 and M_2 are the mass (in grams) of the aerospace vessel and of the Secondary Image, and r is the Image projection distance in centimeters. The second equation, $F = K \dfrac{Q_1Q_2}{r^2}$, was given to us by the great French investigator Charles Coulomb in 1785—exactly 200 years ago—and is his Law of Electrostatic Charges. It is the foundation of the present theory of Electricity. In our P.M.I. Propulsion application, the value of the product $K Q_1Q_2$ is determined by the modulation density of Rayform 37^5, which carries the magnetic number attributes of the Secondary Image *materia*. From these two related formulas, applied to the propulsion of a 1.01 GeeForce 1,000-ton Heavy Transport, we have collected actual field test data that verify that the nominal, net-positive attractive force acting on the aerospace vessel is 9×10^{11} dynes of absolute thrust—or 1,010 tons of conventional (gravitational) thrust.

Now, if you will retain these figures for a moment, we will consider a remarkable similiarity: Since 1968, when LGM #1, the first Pulsar, was discovered by the Cambridge Observatory, astronomers have been amazed at the precise timing of the radio frequency signals that come from these distant celestial bodies. Pulsars, as you know, are composed of material whose atoms have absorbed their electrons into the central protons, forming the most dense of elemental substances—the neutrons. By 1984—16 years after LGM #1—more than a thousand Pulsars have been identified in the heavens, and their sizes and densities have been accurately gauged to the characteristics of their radio pulses. The larger, less dense White Dwarf Pulsars—"only" a few million tons per *cubic inch*—send out beeps that range up to 2 seconds in duration. But the tremendously compact Neutron-Pulsar Stars, with *densities of more than a billion tons per cubic inch,* and spinning at extreme rotational velocities, squirt out rf beeps only 5 to 10 milli-seconds in duration. A Neutron Star with a 10 milli-second beep is estimated by Pulsar astronomers to be a billion ton per cubic inch compressed star, 18 miles in diameter, whose origin was once a celestial giant two or three times the size of our own Sun. Truly, the Pulsars are marvels of Nature that challenge human understanding.

In our discussion today we have referred to the Secondary Image in P.M.I. Propulsion technology as being a Neutron Image. And we say this with purpose—not alone because the Neutron Image also challenges our understanding, but because it shares a remarkable and special point of identity with the celestial Neutron-Pulsars. For example, from the Secondary Image of a mock-up 1,000-ton Heavy Transport vessel throttled to nominal 1.01 GeeForce, we receive radio frequency beeps whose characteristics are exactly those of a Pulsar. The broadband rf beep from the Secondary Image of our 1,000-ton test vessel has a precise duration of 231 nano-seconds, and the pulses repeat at absolutely constant intervals of 31,231 nano-seconds (31.231 micro-seconds).

Based on data in the *World Astronomical Society's Catalog of Pulsar Observations and Correlations,* our Heavy Transport's pulsating signal suggests that, indeed, we are looking at an Image that resembles a small Neutron mass, in the billion ton per cubic inch category. Our previously verified attraction force of 9×10^{11} dynes on the drawpin of the 1,000-ton Heavy Transport tells us—from $F = G \dfrac{M_1 M_2}{r^2}$ — that M_2, the Secondary Image mass needed to produce this amount of attractive force (1.01 Gee-Force or 1 percent greater than Earth gravity effect on the vessel) calculates out to 2×10^{13} *tons.* When we now put these numbers together—the 2×10^{13} ton mass and the 10^9 (one billion) ton per cubic inch density—simple division yields the finished portrait of the fabulous Attractor. She—or it—our Neutron Image, is a spherically shaped—shall we say—*something,* 2.8 feet in diameter, at a definite point in projection ahead of us. But still, it is completely invisible to our sight, and probably would not impede us one ounce if we were to walk directly through it. Therefore, in spite of this carefully resolved "picture," we must keep in mind— from a solid ground, down-to-Earth viewpoint—that there are only three realities about this fantastic analytic Secondary Image:

1. It emits *rf* beeps from a definite point out in front of our

vessel, which we assume to be its Projected-Transposed location.

2. The Image exerts a net-positive attraction force on the aerospace vessel, in proportion to the product of their independent magnetic masses, and in inverse proportion to the square of the Image distance ahead of the vessel.

3. We can control Propulsion GeeForce by regulating the values of Image magnetic mass M_2, and distance r, according to

$$F = G \frac{M_1 M_2}{r^2}$$; and by adjusting the product value of $Q_1 Q_2$ in

$$F = K \frac{Q_1 Q_2}{r^2} .$$

Perhaps we should note that Newton's equation of Universal Attraction could be applied in a study of any of our common mechanical-motive processes. As a statement of the force applied in an automotive or jet aircraft propulsion problem, or even in the mechanics of ordinary walking, we could set down a numerical equivalent, expressed in terms of the concentrated attractive mass of a proximate body. If such an analogy were to serve a technical or analytical end, it could be readily calculated. After all, an expression in these numbers would be just an extension of our imaginations into an alternate physical and mathematical representation. Yet, in a particular way, the Neutron Image analogy suits P.M.I. Technology. From a most unconventional three-step staging of EM Rayform techniques, P.M.I. Technology achieves a positive and real end-result: Propulsion. We understand reasonably well the activities in the Projection and in the Attraction stages. These involve straightforward Rayform processes—straightforward at least to our EM P.M.I. Research crew who now have had some 30 years of daily association with them. But the middle stage—the Transitional passage of *status* from the Primary to the Secondary Image—is another matter.

I am reminded of our dedicatory preambles 30 years ago, in which we criticized society's acceptance of technologies that are founded on scientific mystery. It is humbling to realize that we are now recommending the development and exploitation of a new technology, parts of which defy logic. Our condescending, willing-to-accept attitude reflects on the very motivations that have fired us. The present scientific situation—one of a deep and promising penetration into the EM Rayform wonder of Nature; with the concomitant failure to solve all of the secrets of multiple universal relativity—surely exemplifies the fringes of Natural mystery that will always be with Science. And which, incidentally, keep us open-minded and in active pursuit.

Perhaps, some day, when more is known of the exact nature of events in the Transition stage, we can talk in and with unimpeachable scientific wisdom. Until that day, we humbly must resort to mathematical analogy—to our Neutron Image—to rationalize the marvelous and real end-result: the wondrous achievement of a new form of propulsion for man.

This short time that it has taken today to relate the EM Scientific Discoveries, in a background to P.M.I. Propulsion hardly does justice to the years of research expanded by my dedicated colleagues. And it is an altogether brief and insignificant introduction compared to the efforts—and perhaps the lifetimes—that need to be devoted toward the successful attainment of a working P.M.I. Propulsion Technology.

We live today, in A.D. 1985, in the most exciting period of change, of "transition," in history. Nature has offered us a renewal of our abused and battered partnership, a new chance for man by revealing the EM Rayform Discoveries in our time. The coming 15 year period of design and development that will bring us to the millennial-year presentation, may be more crucial to mankind's future than the EM Discoveries, themselves. In launching this future—for P.M.I. Technology, for EM Science, and most importantly, for world peace and harmony—we must all share in this gravest, and yet, most promising opportunity ever offered to all the inhabitants of our Earth."

Plum Brook, Ohio, U.S.A.
April, A.D. 1985
William Josephs

P.M.I. AEROSPACE VESSEL DESIGN CRITERIA
and PERFORMANCE EXPECTATIONS
—from an EM Science Journal Technical Paper,
dated A.D. 1997

Three years before the demonstration of P.M.I. Propulsion to the world in A.D. 2000, a farsighted Technical Paper on the subject of Aerospace Design was published in the *Journal of EM Science*. The Journal is preserved and included in the Archives of EM History, which has also been our source for William Josephs' Plum Brook address of A.D. 1985. The subject Aerospace Vessel Design Criteria Paper of 1997 is particularly significant and of interest to modern 30th century space travelers, because it describes vessel design parameters based on a series of arbitrary flight-path restrictions. Both the original principles of aerospace design, and the flight space restrictions have carried over into our own time, 10 centuries later.

Most of the subsequent account of the pioneer days of P.M.I. Technology draws upon information related in this highly regarded A.D. 1997 Technical Paper. Some paragraphs of our story are directly copied from the Paper, as we attempt to relive those exciting first days of our most dynamic EM Technology.

*   *   *

Following Plum Brook—it is obvious, from the A.D. 1997 EM Science Journal Technical Paper—a rampant enthusiasm and industry promoted the rapid evolution of the 100 P.M.I. prototypes. We learn that the first series of P.M.I. prototype test flights took place in 1995, only 10 years after the announcement of the EM Discoveries. While the 1997 Technical Paper sticks close to its principal subject, vessel design and flight performance, it does make a notation of an unexpected scientific bonus observed on a test mission of a P.V. (Personal Vehicular) aerospace vessel in 1996. At flight level 17,800 miles—the Paper reveals—the P.M.I.-P.V. experienced a sudden acceleration produced by an unforeseen but exact .0346 GeeForce. The aerospace vessel's Projected Magnetic Secondary Image acted as if all remaining Earth gravity effect had suddenly vanished. The sharp increase in Image Attraction—it was later realized—was indeed exactly equivalent to the remaining Earth gravity effect at that altitude. The little prototype P.V. aerospace vessel had stumbled into man's first contact with the P.M.I. Lach 1: GRAVITY coincidence. From the observations recorded on this pioneer test mission, EM scientists and technologists, before the end of the 20th century, were able to derive a prediction of eventual aerospace travel-velocities that would exceed the speed of light.

[The P.V. 1-ton aerospace vessel on its testing mission in A.D. 1966 was actually detecting the Lach 1 barrier line. The Lach 1, or light speed 1, barrier for Magnetic Image Propulsion Systems occurs at points in space where the combined gravitational pull of proximate planets, moons, stars, and the like falls below 1.116 feet per second^2—a value equal to .0346 g. (g., the effect of Earth gravity at sea level, is 32.2 feet per second^2.) The Lach 1 barrier value of gravitational pull, 1.116 feet per second^2, is frequently called nano-gravity, since—in numerical similarity— 1.116 feet is the exact distance that light travels in 1 nano-second (10^{-9} second). Observation of this related behavior of light and GRAVITY had great meaning and bearing on the future of space travel. Eventually, by the 25th century, man's command of multiple light velocities reached the Lach 10^3 level, or 1,000 times the speed of light. The perfection, a century earlier, of GRAVITY feedback technologies in Coincidence with multiple Lach velocities made it feasible for space vessels—and their human passengers— mally would be sustained in reaching exponential Lach speeds. It to zero out the extreme "G" stresses or GeeForce effects that nor- was in the Lach 10^3 era that voyages to Alpha Centauri, 4 ⅓ light years distant, became a routine 3-day round trip. Even brilliant Sirius at 8.7 light years could be visited within a week. Our present Lach 10^5 level of attainment for P.M.I. aerospace travel, achieved only 50 years ago, has opened the entire Milky Way Galaxy to our adventurous explorers. However, it is still an arduous 2-year round journey to the Galaxy's outer reaches, some 90,000 light years into the depths of the Universe.]

P.M.I. Propulsion force-capabilities—the 1997 Design Criteria Paper begins—are usually not as sensational and as demonstrative as those employed in rocket propulsion. Many military ballistic missiles utilize short time (100 second) firings that develop thrusts well in excess of 10 GeeForce. Even the masterpiece of rocket engineering, the Saturn 5-Apollo spacecraft, blasts off with a mightly thrust of 3,750 tons, or 1.25 GeeForce. But the 2,300 ton Saturn first stage lives only for 2 minutes, burning up fuel at close to 20 tons per second. And then, at 40 miles altitude and having thrust its burden to an initial velocity of 6,000 MPH, it is finished —and abandoned. The second and third stages, in succession, boost final velocity to 25,000 MPH; and they, too, are jettisoned. Apollo, the 45-ton remaining payload that journeys to the moon, is less than 1½ percent of the total weight of the Saturn 3-stage propulsion system.

In contrast, a P.M.I. 1,000-ton Heavy Transport departs from its moorings in complete silence, with tortoise-like initial velocity, and without the least bit of smoke from its minimal 1.01 Gee-Force Attraction machinery. It takes almost 2 minutes for it to reach 100 MPH velocity, and it is only at the 7-mile level when it actually throttles back to maintain this base departure velocity. Heavy Transport is in no hurry to escape the atmosphere, mainly because it does not have to resort to violent speeds to aid its escape from gravity or from a fuel-load dilemma. The P.M.I.-H.T.'s unsensational, but highly efficient, lift-off pace illustrates the completely sensible flight performance options that characterize the P.M.I. vessel. Unlike the rocket-propelled vessel, which is primarily a space coaster; the P.M.I. aerospace craft drives forward continually with full-time, moderate-thrust propulsion. It is a 100% payload vessel, not encumbered by fuel weight. Every ounce—practically speaking—that goes out comes back.

The propulsion capabilities offered by the Projected Magnetic Image System permit vessel designs of the simplest and most useful configurations. It is convenient to consider these capabilities in terms of what a P.M.I. vessel does not have to do—with reference, of course, to the design confinements imposed by rocket thrust propulsion:

● A P.M.I. vessel does not have to burn up its fuel as rapidly as possible, for the purpose of reducing its own weight. The effective mass of a P.M.I. vessel upon which the propulsion force operates is practically constant. And the equally steady thrust, developed by the P.M.I.'s Attraction stage, moves this mass at a fixed value of acceleration.

● A P.M.I. vessel does not have to gain velocity as rapidly as possible in order to minimize the time that gravity works against the vessel's vertical effort. Since there is no real concern for the depletion of fuel—its counter-gravity energy capability—the net gain in velocity achieved by propulsion over gravitation becomes simply a function of travel time in the vertical component of flight.

● A P.M.I. vessel does not have to rely on the centrifugal force of an orbital trajectory to aid its opposition to Earth gravity. The P.M.I.'s continuous, full-time propulsion-force capability, in excess of the force of gravity, makes it unnecessary to accelerate rapidly through the lower atmosphere and to divert at high velocity into a horizontal course component for the purpose of attaining orbital position.

Because it has complete mastery over gravity, without having to utilize high speeds in anti-gravity flight techniques, the P.M.I. aerospace ship—from a design viewpoint—can adapt its size, shape, and performance more directly to its ultimate mission. Aerodynamic resistance, or drag—which varies in proportion to air density and also in proportion to the square of the vessel's velocity through the atmosphere—remains as the only considerable factor limiting a complete freedom in vessel design and flight performance. Each of the four P.M.I. models, from the 1,000-ton Heavy Transport to the 1-ton Personal Vehicular, has its own particular external shape and internal structure. These determinate design characteristics represent the best categorical utility that a reasonable compromise with drag effect allows. And only the

P.M.I. aerospace vessel, neither a beholder to gravity nor to velocity, can make this compromise.

THE P.M.I. H.T.-1000 HEAVY TRANSPORT

The Heavy Transport, whose mission is to haul bulk cargo, elects to minimize aerodynamic drag by keeping its velocity on low altitude (atmospheric) voyages to a 100 MPH maximum. This sizable concession to speed permits the 1,000-tonner to be built along the rougher structural lines that favor cargo handling. The H.T.-1000 boasts a 10 to 1 gross to tare weight ratio, allowing a full 900 tons cargo capacity. At the relatively slow 100 MPH speed limit, operational efficiency of these freighter types is not greatly impaired, since even this limiting velocity is adequate to the nature of their service. Of course, at drag-free extra-atmospheric levels—above 100 miles altitude—these bulky square-shaped barges, like all P.M.I. propelled space vessels, have no velocity restraints.

On long hauls around the Earth, the 1.01 GeeForce H.T.-1000 will sometimes find it advantageous to proceed to the 100-mile extra-atmospheric level where it will enter a controlled sub-orbital course to its destination. At the 100-mile altitude level, Earth's gravity effect has dropped only 1%, to 31.9 feet per second^2; but even this small increment that can now be added to the vessel's horizontal thrust effort is most welcome and remarkably effective. Having leveled off at 100-mile altitude, on a typical 12,000-mile journey—halfway around the globe—the Heavy Transport's 1.01 GeeForce, resolved into vectors of .99 GeeForce anti-gravity component (31.9 ft/sec^2 acceleration equivalent) and .19 GeeForce horizontal thrust (6.15 ft/sec^2), will carry the vessel to an amazing peak horizontal velocity of 12,500 MPH at mid-journey. In an equal 6,000-mile on-course deceleration leg, the 1,000-ton freighter slows down to zero horizontal velocity just as it arrives above its port of destination. The H.T.-1000 then descends vertically through the atmosphere, never exceeding its atmospheric base speed of 100 MPH. Total elapsed time for the 12,000-mile cargo run is 4 hours, including an hour up to altitude and another hour back down to its unloading dock.

But the paramount effect of *full-time,* moderate-thrust P.M.I. Propulsion is dramatically and conclusively shown on an H.T.-1000's routine voyage to the Earth's moon. This 240,000-mile journey in drag-free space logs in at only 6½ hours elapsed time from Earth dock to Moon dock—only 2½ hours more than the 12,000-mile cargo-haul half circle around the globe. The secret to the amazing 6½-hour time for this great journey lies in the diminishing effect of gravity as the aerospace vessel climbs out from Earth. Gravity effect decreases inversely as the square of the distance from the Earth's center. Moreover, at and beyond the 18,000-mile altitude, it is now known and verified that P.M.I. Propulsion Systems lose all remaining gravitational effect resulting from proximate-body attraction. From that point in space (or any equivalent point subject to less than 1.116 feet per second² gravity effect) a P.M.I. System's nominal GeeForce contributes totally to the vessel's absolute or universal velocity.

Thus, Moon-bound and enjoying its release from gravity, the space freighter reaches an amazing 125,000 MPH top speed, midway between Earth and Moon; before beginning its deceleration and let-down. So agile has it become in space with its full-time 1.01 GeeForce—which barely lifted it from its Earth dock—the 1,000-ton Transport could easily make six round trips to the Moon in the time that it takes 45-ton Apollo to coast along on a one-way traverse. It is obvious that the P.M.I. H.T.-1000's compromising 100-MPH maximum atmospheric velocity hardly affects its over-all efficiency. And its nearly drag-free flight through the lower 100-mile air space allows H.T.-1000 to be designed and built as a full-service cargo vessel for either atmospheric or interplanetary assignment.

THE P.M.I. M.C.-100 MEDIUM COMMERCIAL

In a somewhat less restrictive concession to atmospheric drag, the 100-ton Medium Commercial P.M.I. aerospace vessel allows itself a 500 MPH top speed in the blanket of air surrounding

Earth. For the privilege of this extra, but still moderate speed, the 1.10 GeeForce M.C.-100 must have finer aerodynamic stream-lining and a heavier over-all structure, both of which detract from cargo capacity. The M.C.-100 has a 5:1 gross to tare ratio, only one-half that of the slower H.T.-1000. But with its 10 times greater initial acceleration capability over the 1,000-ton Heavy, the M.C.-100 can reach base departure velocity in only 4 minutes. In another 10 minutes—in a vertical departure—it can break out of the atmosphere, free and clear, at the 100-mile level. Still not a spectacular departure compared to mighty Saturn-Apollo; but M.C.-100's 500 MPH limit gets it on its way in a business-like fashion.

With its ample and sufficient atmospheric speed, the P.M.I. Medium Commercial category will find frequent assignment to short, cross-country deliveries, which are best routed along the low-altitude skyways. The penalty the 100-ton Medium pays in loss of cargo volume and in the first cost of its streamlined struc-ture is small in relation to its service value in the Earth's highly restrictive airspace. And on extra-atmospheric voyages, the M.C.-100's full-time 1.10 GeeForce and its swept-back contours will carry special cargos, or more than 300 passengers, in luxurious style. It will clear Earth gravity effect at the 18,000 mile level in 45 minutes, traveling through that Zero "g" Marker at 13 miles per second—48,000 MPH. On a lunar course, the sleek 100-tonner will continue in acceleration to Earth-Moon mid-point at a full-effective 35.4 feet/sec^2. Maximum velocity at the accel.-decel. mid-point is 130,000 MPH; actually not much greater than that managed by its big brother, the "slow" H.T.-1000 freighter.

The similar space-velocity capabilities of M.C. and H.T. illus-trate the over-riding effect of Earth gravity on their net available propulsion thrust. Below the 100-mile altitude level, the 1.10 GeeForce Medium Commercial has 10 times, or 1000% as much excess thrust over gravity as the 1.01 GeeForce Heavy Transport. But, in gravity-free space beyond the 18,000-mile level, the M.C.'s thrust exceeds the H.T.'s by only 9%. When gravity leaves, the two vessels—at nominal throttle settings—run almost side-by-side. Still, an M.C. that leaves its Earth dock at the same time as a Heavy Transport, will arrive on the Moon in a short 4 hours, beating the Heavy's pace by 2½ hours. Most of the M.C.'s gain, of course, is made in its 10-minute, 100-mile lift-off from Earth, and in the equivalent descent to the Moon dock. The H.T.-1000 Heavy Transport requires a full hour for each of these 100-mile stages. It should be pointed out that all P.M.I. vessels will duplicate their standard Earth take-off and landing procedures, even on the atmosphere-free Moon, and under the one-sixth gravitational conditions found there. A uniform flight operational procedure for each P.M.I. vessel category will promote safety and simplify traffic control in the years to come, not only on Earth but throughout the Solar planetary system.

THE M.C.-100 EXPLORERS
—OVER THE HORIZON TO JUPITER AND SATURN

Ten special M.C.-100 × 3.03 deep-space prototypes equipped with powerful 3.03 GeeForce propulsion plants will soon bring the planets to our very doorsteps. Designed specifically to operate in the vicinity of giant Jupiter with its 2.64 times greater gravity than Earth, the 100-ton "Explorer" spaceships will have tremendous reserve for operations on the smaller planets and moons. The deep-space M.C.-100's will have quarters for 20 scientists and technicians, and will be fitted out with provisions and accommodations for voyages of a year's duration.

The first fully complemented Explorer voyage to Jupiter is scheduled to depart within the next five years, perhaps as early as 2001, after the M.C.-100 × 3.03 protoypes have been thoroughly proven. But already, there is sufficient performance data derived from the early test runs of Explorer to bring forward some amazing velocity and timing predictions for the Jupiter traverse. Actually, the 3.03 nominal GeeForce thrust engineered into the 100-ton Explorers is much more than is need for inter-planetary travel, in view of the full-time-continuous rating of P.M.I. Propulsion plants, and of the preference to maintain at least 1.00 GeeForce on the vessel systems and personnel. It is likely that nominal thrust will be used only for short durations, and in Jupiter approach and departure operations where it is mandatory. Some thought is being given to programming several different levels of thrust during a voyage-day, so that a 24-hour average of perhaps 1.50 or even 2.00 GeeForce would be experienced by the crew. Even this physical burden over a day's span would call for an utmost human endurance and courage.

An interesting note, with regard to our prospective Jupiter mission, is that a continuous and ideally comfortable 1 GeeForce will do almost as fine a job of getting the vessel to its destination as would a physically unbearable, continuous 3 GeeForce. This, of course, is due to the fact that the velocity developed on a space mission is a function of both the acceleration (or deceleration) and the total distance traveled.

$$V^2\text{peak} = 2\ as \quad V\text{peak} = \sqrt{2\ as} \quad V\text{average} = \frac{\sqrt{2\ as}}{2}$$

Thus, the spaceship's velocity increases only in proportion to the square root of the acceleration corresponding to a fixed GeeForce throttle position. At the improbable 3.03 nominal GeeForce, the Medium Commercial Explorer could make the Jupiter transit in a rapid 3½ days; whereas, at a comfortable 1 GeeForce acceleration—where everyone on board retains his Earthly weight, figure, and composure—the Explorer will arrive in exactly 6 days. A worthwhile trade of 2½ days for vital human comforts, and still not too bad an elapsed time; considering that giant Jupiter lies 366 million miles out in space—more than 1,500 times the distance covered in an Earth to Earth-Moon flight. What is equally astonishing, as a result of full-time-continuous 1.00 GeeForce P.M.I. thrust, is the maximum velocity that is achieved midway on the journey—a neat 5,050,000 MPH. If it were possible to travel at low altitude around the Earth at this rate, such a rounder would take 18 seconds!

It is, perhaps, worth our while to pause on our passage to Jupiter, to make a note of man's pace of progress in the newly born EM Science and in its Propulsion Technologies. Only 10 years ago, at the zenith of the era of propulsion via rocketry, the best estimated time for a considered—but never attempted—manned journey to Jupiter was 2½ years, and close to 6 years if the durable adventurer dared to "coast on" to the next stop—Saturn. Soon, a 100-ton P.M.I. Explorer will open the 21st century by shortening the 2½-year Jupiter run to a comfortable and remarkable 6 days—an improvement of 150 times over. Some 500 years ago in A.D. 1492, we recall from our history books that Cristóbal Colón's resolute armada of "Explorers" reached the New World of the Americas by sailing the unknown Atlantic Ocean in 60 suspense-filled days. As we close 5 centuries of time since the 100-ton *Santa Maria*'s inspired voyage, modern jet-age trans-Atlantic flagships overtrace that first 2-month crossing in an easy 10 hours—an improvement of 150 times over.

Quite possibly there is more of dreams than logic in continuing such an analogy, but if Jupiter is to be a "New World"—or one of many—in our destiny, we have not long to wait, to find out. Within the decade, and under the beacon of the Almighty Navigator, another 100-ton *Santa Maria,* this time P.M.I.-propelled, will set sail to bring our technological speculations and the realities of the Universe into coincidence.

The most recent deep-space probes correlated with the best astro-physical estimates of Jupiter indicate that the giant planet, itself, may not be hospitable to human life form because of its dense methane-ammonia atmosphere. However, there is great expectation that at least two of Jupiter's 12 satellite moons—Io and Ganymede—have resolved their insalubrious primordial mantles into nitrogen-oxygen atmospheres, as did our own Earth a billion or so years ago. Io, 2,020 miles in diameter, is a duplicate of our Moon, in size and in satellitic radius from the "mother" planet that holds her in orbit. And equally beautiful but larger Ganymede, which is 40% the size of Earth, will be a certain attraction for exploration and even colonization within the present generation. Because these two living and breathing daughters of Jupiter so closely resemble Earth in atmospheric composition, there is well-considered anticipation that our Explorer pioneers may be greeted, upon landing, by man's Io and Ganymede counterparts. Who, or What, and How they may be is as fascinating to ponder as the voyage itself.

Beyond Jupiter, but at more than double the distance from Earth, awaits beautiful triple-ringed Saturn. Surely, after breaking the space "ice" with successful, manned missions to Jupiter, we shall be eager to set off in pursuit of the second largest satellite of the Sun. There are some most interesting and enticing opportunities in the realm of Saturn. Imagine a planet with a surface area 100 times greater than Earth's, and with a diameter equal to 3 times our equatorial circumference—but still, with a comfortable gravity condition only 10% stronger than our own. But alas, Saturn, like its giant Jovian brother, has not had sufficient time—since the Solar planetary formation 6 billion years ago—to synthesize a nitrogen-oxygen cover from its perpetual inundation of methane and ammonia. In fact, many observers believe that Saturn, even more so than Jupiter, has a planestrial nature constituted of a system of dense gases, rather than upon a solid rock or liquid base. But the exact degree of the Sixth planet's inhospitality, and the extent of its inhuman ambients into all of its vast regions, are yet to be positively and finally written. Nevertheless, prudence suggests that the initial landings and explorations into Saturn's domain head for 3 of the 10 satellite moons that whip around the ammonia-ringed mother planet. Diminutive Rhea (810 miles in diameter) and Dione (550 miles in diameter) are known to have partial pressure atmospheres of oxygen and nitrogen that could be an aid to human life support. And hefty Titan, the twin of Jupiter's Ganymede, may prove to be the most receptive among Saturn's ample family. Recent fly-by photo reconnaissance achieved in the joint U.S.A.-U.S.S.R. Mariner-Zond series has depicted luxuriant vegetation and abundant water on Titan, and an indication of an 80% relative Earth-oxygen supply.

Although the EM Science Council has elected to send our first P.M.I. Medium Commercial Explorers to Jupiter, the marvel of fulltime-continuous 1 GeeForce Propulsion makes the alternate Saturn destination almost a toss-up choice. Our present nascent state of unfamiliarity with fulltime acceleration on missions of great distance inhibits a comprehension that Saturn could be attained in only 8½ days, just 2½ days more than a Jupiter voyage. Yet truly, the 8½ days en route along the 743 million miles is a mathematical certainty based on the great velocity of 7,200,000 MPH—greater than 1% of the speed of light—that will be logged as Explorer passes through the orbit circle of Jupiter, at the half-way mark to Saturn. It is only natural and human to wonder what unforeseen problems our Explorer space crews will encounter at these magnificent velocities. We do know that the greater the spacecraft's speed, the stronger is its commitment to its course. But even this concern becomes minor in view of the extraordinary accuracy and reliability of the latest Mark 10^6 Inertial Navigator, which will guide and lock Explorer, within $1/1,000,000$ of a degree, onto its target point on the celestial navigational sphere. In further reassurance to the Jupiter and Saturn pioneers, astronomers agree that any danger of an interception with wandering meteoric fragments or asteroids is totally inconsequential—and "even less so," they say, with greater spacecraft velocities and their related shorter transit times through the vastness and void of space.

Interplanetary travel aboard the P.M.I. M.C.-100 Explorer will drive home the tremendous quantitative effect of the unit 1.00 GeeForce. Because we ourselves, as human beings, are accustomed to the 1 GeeForce of planet Earth's environment, we tend to relate heavy working effort and tiring tasks to physical stress beyond the comfortable sensation of 1 GeeForce gravity. Indeed, on Earth, 1 GeeForce is nothing more than our own bodily weight, and only contributes to holding us in place on the globe. We are not even aware of the phenomenon. But in gravity-free space, 1 GeeForce with its 32.2 feet per second^2 acceleration, is a tremendous giant of force. In an Earth to space relative sense, if a man on Earth possessed the strength that he does in space—or the effect of that strength—he would be a muscular Goliath, tipping the scales at close to 6,000 pounds. And the same comparison applies to man's machinery. The full-time, moderate-thrust 1.00 GeeForce P.M.I. aerospace vessel, in its space environ, becomes a mammoth indefatigable bird, easily capable of carrying us to Saturn in 8½ hours, and of winging along in absolute comfort at 7,200,000 MPH. But the real marvel to ponder is man himself, who—it provocatively turns out—is ideally constituted to take part in this full-time 1 GeeForce interplanetary exercises. Man is virtually a superman in space. He is a powerful and durable 1 GeeForce athletic specimen housing an intellect and will that transcend his Earthly roots. Can it be a mere coincidence that the physiological evolution of the human species, during all of man's historical time on his 1 GeeForce planet has so well adapted him for this new interplanetary responsibility?

An ebullient, all-out optimism has lately taken over the camp of P.M.I. Propulsion. In particular, flight test data on the M.C.-100 Explorer has instilled a confidence in the Jupiter project that has P.M.I. scientists and technologists predicting a rapid and progressive success. In complete assurance, these enthusiastic visionaries tell us that the M.C.-100 voyages to Jupiter and Saturn will become "among the easier feats that man has applied himself to." Already by quarter century, in A.D. 2025, they see regular commercial runs of sections, divisions, and even fleets of M-C.-100's serving a chain of expanding colonies on dozens of habitable environs throughout the Solar System. They look upon the upcoming Jupiter-Explorer expeditions as the beginning of man's boundless future in space; a future—they are quick to point out—that was endowed to the millennial generation by the stalwart pioneers of rocketry propulsion. For it was at Kennedy-Canaveral and at Kazakhskaya that rocketry released man from the imprisonment of Earth gravity. Nostalgically, but not without reason and meaning, most of today's EM Age visionaries will agree that 99% of the job that will lead us eventually to Jupiter and Saturn was accomplished by the rocketeers who broke gravity. The remaining 1% is attributed to the simple expedient of full-time 1 GeeForce P.M.I. Propulsion.

L.C.-10   and   P.V.-1
THE P.M.I. LIGHT COMMERCIAL AND PERSONAL VEHICULAR CATEGORIES

The general purpose vehicles of the 21st century will be the P.M.I. 1.50 GeeForce Light Commercial and Personal Vehicular aerospace vessels. These two smaller design categories of the

P.M.I. series will surely revolutionize the total concept of transportation. Many EM Age forecasters believe that, by mid-century, the L.C.-10 and the P.V.-1 will constitute 90% of the transportation equipment in use throughout the world. They suggest, with cold technical dispassion, that the highway systems and even the ocean lanes of the world soon will be sparcely used. And, they further advise that terrestrial automotive types, which utilize gravitational adhesion as a basic principle of their design and performance, will become impractical, inefficient, and hopelessly outmoded in the P.M.I. Transportation Age.

Because L.C.-10 and P.V.-1 are primarily to be used in internal atmospheric service or on close-in sub-orbital routes con- necting points around the globe, these high performance designs have been constructed along extremely fine aerodynamic lines, and have been equipped with adequate P.M.I. Propulsion plants to match them to their spheres of operation. For operational safety, and to achieve a satisfactory balance between atmospheric drag and vessel structure, the 10-ton Light Commercial and the 1-ton Personal Vehicular will conform to velocity maximums on all flights through the lower 100 miles of Earth airspace. The L.C.-10, the light cargo and "Greyhound" passenger carrier, is limited to 750 MPH in the atmosphere. And the flashy P.V.-1 four-seater sedan must restrict itself to an even 1,000 MPH.

Both categories of these lightweight, highly mobile aerospace vessels have 1:2:3 fineness or streamline ratios, a geometric design feature that gives them the greatest possible advantage in combatting aerodynamic resistance. On its centerline—in 1:2:3 fineness ratio—the P.V. measures 5 feet tall, 10 feet wide, and 15 feet bow to stern. In an all-round profile as well as in plan views, the 1-ton sedan displays a perfect gibbous or double-convex-lens shape, with sharply tapered identical nose and tail features. The Light Commercial "Greyhound" has ten times the displacement of its twin in mini-design and manages to fit this 10-ton bulk into exactly three times the P.V.'s dimensions. L.C.-10 shapes out in a 15-foot height, 30-foot width, and 45-foot length. In a side-by-side comparison with the sharply profiled Personal Vehicular sedan, "Greyhound" presents a modified gibbous shape in all views, being more blunt in the areas near its nose and tail. The somewhat lower velocity restriction of 750 MPH permits the more bulbous outline, which in turn improves cargo stowage facility— and passenger headroom. Both categories are structurally stressed for 10 G's, and are completely enveloped in stout heat-shielded exteriors to provide maximum safety in the event of an orbital spin-out or an inadvertent atmospheric speed run. But the fine streamlining, the safety shielding, and their extra sturdy 10 G. construction are not without cost. Because of them, the L.C.-10 and the P.V.-1 have rather inefficient gross to tare ratios of only 2:1. This value, of course, is low in comparison to the 10:1 of the Heavy Transport and even the 5:1 of the 100-ton Medium Commercial. But a smaller working load is the price that must be paid for high-speed operation in the Earth's atmosphere.

FSFR and MSFR
FULL SQUARES and MODIFIED SQUARES

In the oncoming era of aerospace travel, it is to be a fundamental precept that airspace traffic regulations not only will allow but will encourage P.M.I. vessels to perform to the full extent of their design potentials. The heavyweight categories, the H.T.'s and the M.C.'s that are slower and that primarily will be on freight hauls will be required to conduct their flights in the "truck lanes" of the controlled airspace. All of their departures, low-level transits, and approaches must proceed along fully squared vertical to horizontal patterns. But FSFR (Full-Square Flight Rules) is not in the least a confinement to them. On their cargo-carrying missions and at their slow confining velocities, the Full-Square traffic pattern actually promotes a systematic and safe flight sequence.

The real gainers under P.M.I. air traffic regulations will be the highly torqued lightweights, the L.C.-10 and the P.V.-1. Their greater speeds and maneuverability earn them the right to option either the Full-Square or the Modified-Square Flight Rules. Under MSFR (Modified-Square Flight Rules) the two lightweight sprinters are permitted to point directly for their destinations, almost from the moment of take-off. In the past two years of P.V. prototype flight testing, the new liberal MSFR traffic regulations already have aided in chalking up some astonishing flight performance records. In fact, the cross-country travel times achieved in both L.C. and P.V. testing are so startling in comparison to the jet flight schedules of the past two decades that the general public may go through some shock as they reach for comprehension of our new P.M.I. Age of travel.

HOLD YOUR HAT, HERE WE GO

On a typical New York to Los Angeles flight an L.C.-10 or a P.V.-1 will have an almost unlimited selection of departure and arrival patterns, en route altitudes, and GeeForce throttle settings. The choice and combination of these flight options will be up to each pilot's preference for time and comfort en route. How about climbing aboard one of the flashy P.V.-1 prototypes, and sharing the excitement of its 1.50 GeeForce as we travel cross-country under a few of the many possible Full-Square and Modified-Square flight plans. There is nothing like getting checked out early in our wondrous new Age of P.M.I. air travel. Are you ready to go? O.K., let's lift off New York for a low level—say 5-mile altitude flight to Los Angeles. We'll climb out at a 30-degree angle on this trip and at nominal 1.5 GeeForce.

Throttle set. Magnetic Image projected correctly, and vectored to 274° true—our great circle course to Los Angeles. Clear? Attraction stage, Energize! We're away.

A thrill of confidence surges through us as we feel the authority and the certainty of the Attraction stage's 3,000 pounds of magnetic thrust. Forward and upward have suddenly become a purpose, a vital part of our being. Departure motion, not unlike that in a smooth, silent, high-speed elevator, wraps its powerful arms around our trim little vessel. And are we leaving New York behind. After only one minute we are more than five miles on our way, and climbing through the three-mile level. Immediately, we adjust projected image position to check our vertical thrust component, so that the P.V.-1 will roll out smoothly onto the five-mile altitude level we have selected in this MSFR flight plan. Just 30 seconds later, 1½ minutes and 10 miles out from New York, we attain 1,000 MPH, our limiting atmospheric velocity. Throttles back to 75% nominal GeeForce, and again, reposition the P.M.I. (the Projected Image) for level flight at 1,000 MPH.

In level flight, unlike a conventional winged aircraft, our P.V.-1 incurs no aerodynamic wing-drag in association with the lift vector that holds our 2,000 pounds at altitude against the pull of gravity. All vertical thrust, or anti-gravity component (1.00 GeeForce for level flight), is furnished by P.M.I. Attraction. And our "super clean" aerospace sedan, endowed with a beautifully low coefficient of parasitic (structural) drag by the 1:2:3 aerodynamic fineness of its all-round, double-convex-lens shape, requires only 1,000 pounds of horizontal thrust—.50 GeeForce for the 1-ton P.V.—to maintain legal cruising limit at the five-mile altitude. The GeeForce vector display board on our instrument panel has now steadied to readouts of 1.10 GeeForce applied, resolved to 1.00 anti-gravity, and .50 horizontal thrust. Straight and level at 1,000 MPH. California, here we come. But—2.8 hours later—the 2,800-mile journey to Los Angeles at 1,000 MPH turns out to be a rather routine, perfectly smooth, "magnetically" silent—bus ride. I hope we don't sound too unappreciative and disappointed, but even the jet-powered SST's of 25 years ago could run circles around that time. Did we take the local interurban instead of the express? Perhaps we did select a flight plan that is more suitable to an L.C.-10 Greyhound trunk-line carrier. Well, at least it was a pleasant, comfortable trip, and for openers, a real confidence builder.

Let us go back to New York and file for a more favorable route. This time we will get our P.V.-1 up and out of the sticky atmosphere, and we'll just see what she can do with the throttles "at the wall" and with no 1,000 MPH velocity restriction to cramp her style. Ready again? Flight Number 2, still MSFR, New York to Los Angeles. On departure we will continue a 30-degree climb-out all the way up to the 100-mile level, roll out smoothly and simultaneously re-apply full nominal 1.50 GeeForce for half the distance to Los Angeles. This means that we will be accelerating at 48.3 feet per second per second all the way to Kansas. There's our clearance from New York Tower. So hold your hat, here we go!

Elapsed time 1½ minutes: Climbing nicely, perfectly smooth and quiet, all gauges indicate normal. Throttles back, to lock in at 1,000 MPH on our 200-mile up-slope through the atmosphere.

Elapsed time 12 minutes: We are nearing flight plan altitude, the 100-mile level. Now, an easy 10-second roll-out onto the plane of our inertial horizon. Harrisburg, Pennsylvania, barely visible off our tailcone, is already behind us as we ease the throttles ahead to nominal 1.50 GeeForce and set the Projected Image position for automatic-level flight with orbital-effect compensation. We are really beginning to move. The instrument panel velocity-readout is spinning so fast that we must reset the counter to broad scale (100 MPH divisions). Every four seconds we click another 100 MPH. After only one minute from roll-out onto flight plan altitude, velocity reads 2,500 MPH—and steadily building. As our trim little P.V. continues to accelerate, we note that we are perfectly comfortable. Our on-board G monitor tells us that we are experiencing a G-force vector-resultant of only .3 G more than we would feel on the ground. And actually, it is a kind of reassuring pressure distributed evenly across the full area of our back and shoulders by the automatic G-force vector-aligning bodyseat. We are confident we could endure, even enjoy, this mild physiological loading for hours, perhaps for days. The roll-out to altitude just a minute ago (a 3 degree per second turn at 1,000 MPH) put us to 2½ G's of physical stress for 10 seconds, and that wasn't even enough to bother us—for that short period. We are beginning to enjoy our high speed environment. We take a minute to pour ourselves a cup of cool water and to gaze spellbound at the beautiful curve of the Earth's horizon, which, at our 100-mile altitude, is some 3,000 miles distant and already beyond our Los Angeles destination. Even during this quiet minute our P.V.'s velocity on course has passed through the 4,000 MPH marker. Say, we're going to be there before we know it!

Elapsed time 21½ minutes: Can you believe it, we are over

Midpoint, Kansas. Velocity readout: 15,000 MPH—after only 9½ minutes of horizontal flight. That's an average velocity for the 1,225-mile level-flight acceleration leg of 8,000 MPH. (We started with 1,000 MPH over Harrisburg.) Now, in the busy minute and 25 seconds that it takes us to cross the 350 nautical miles of Kansas, we adjust ourselves and our vessel to the 1.50 GeeForce deceleration leg. P.M.I. repositioned to an equivalent projection astern; bodyseats reoriented to place the reversed net-resultant G's on our backs; throttles maintained on 1.50 nominal. It's an easy turn-around—as we begin to lose velocity.

Elapsed time 31 minutes: Here we are, slowed down again to 1,000 MPH. From Midpoint, Kansas, deceleration has its hold on us for another short 9½ minutes, matching the time and distance of the acceleration leg. We nose downward through the atmospheric re-entrance point. There are 12 minutes to go to "touchdown." Our dauntless little P.V.-1 relaxes at approximately 70% throttle as it holds itself to the 1,000 MPH restricted velocity on our 30-degree glideslope. We begin to recognize landmarks in the beautiful Mojave Desert passing below us, and there's the San Gabriel Mountains just ahead.

Elapsed time 43 minutes: Docking. P.M.I. Attraction stage, de-energize. All switches off. Hello, Los Angeles.

43 minutes. Not too bad a time; and considerably better than the 2 hour and 48 minute low-altitude run. Well, we sure went to school on Flight Number 2. Now that we know where the P.V.-1 runs best, we could probably shave a few more minutes from our total elapsed time by filing another flight plan, in which we would point the P.V.'s nose straight up, following the "truck lane" to the 100-mile level. On the way, we might even pass a few 1,000-ton Heavy Transports chugging along at their restricted 100 MPH atmospheric velocities. Eight minutes after take-off, on this new "run for a record" flight plan, we would top out of our 100-mile vertical climb, with a 2½ G., standard 3 degree/second roll-out onto course 274. The 1,400 miles to Kansas would slip by in a fast 10 minutes. And we attain a midpoint velocity of 17,000 MPH, 2,000 better than we were able to build up in our previous, but shorter, level stretch from Harrisburg. Decelera-

tion and downslope approach legs, matching the first half of the
ride, would be equivalent 10 and 8 minutes episodes. Total elapsed
time: 36 minutes dock to dock. That is about the best time we
could manage within the nominal limits of our little 1-ton Personal
Vehicular aerospace sedan.

Most travelers in our upcoming P.M.I. era will prefer the
convenience and additional comfort of a little longer elapsed time
on the N.Y.-L.A. trip. An MSFR flight plan calling for a 1-hour,
10-minute cross-country in-flight time has been proposed for this
"no hurry" group of private P.V. operators. The flight route,
patterned after the 36-minute record-time itinerary, will be
straight up, but with a reduced speed roll-out at the 100-mile
top. At no time during the entire ride will a throttle setting
greater than 1.10 GeeForce be used. Because of the personal
comfort features of the 1-hour, 10-minute flight, Light Commercial
L.C.-10 Greyhounds, each carrying 50 passengers, have adopted
this Modified-Square Flight Plan for their "Express" service between coasts.

Aboard a P.V.-1 or an Express Greyhound on the 2,800-mile
level-flight leg of this popular flight plan, the traveler, as he would
in any moving vehicle, shares the "sensation" of the force vectors
directed in anti-gravity and in horizontal propulsion. But the
P.M.I. passenger experiences a special case of body action and
reaction, different from that in a conventional jet aircraft or reac-
tion-powered spacecraft. In P.M.I. vessels, a passenger must
adapt himself to the phenomenon of magnetic pull, or P.M.I.
Attraction. Because the body weight of the passenger is an integral
component of the total attractive mass of the P.M.I. aerospace
vessel—and is included in the propulsion-producing

$$G = \frac{M_1 M_2}{r^2}$$

Gravitation Force Equation (as part of M_1)—the "involved"
passenger finds himself being pulled toward the Projected Magnetic Image in the same direction as the force vector. And this
is an experience contrary to his usual force-reaction sensation.
In conventional vehicles and vessels, the occupant is truly a

free-body within a shell and does not contribute to the propulsion, as he does under Projected Magnetic Image Attraction.

And so, as we accelerate comfortably toward Kansas, the net physical effect on the traveler, after deducting the anti-gravity vector, will be an average horizontal thrust of .60 Gee-Force. Passengers and crew will enjoy partial weightlessness. A 175-pounder, for example, will feel like he is carrying a body weight of only 100 pounds as he "stands" horizontally with feet pointing to California and head to New York. Of course, all passengers will have to sit tight in their automatic bodyseats during P.M.I. repositioning for deceleration over Kansas. But at least, on the 1-hour, 10-minute, 1.10 GeeForce ride—despite the confusion of the heads or feet-first attitudes—there will be a few extra moments to relax or to sip a cup of coffee, tea, or milk. And, no doubt, there will be many professional travelers who will enjoy a brief nap—possibly to dream over and over about this veritable wonder of being "transposed" to the opposite side of the country.

WELL, HELLO THERE
—TO TWO FRIENDLY TRAVELING COMPANIONS

Obviously, the secret of shorter cross-country travel time lies in getting up and out of the atmosphere, where the aerospace vessel's peak velocity is limited only by its P.M.I. acceleration potential, and by the halfway distance to its destination. But also, as you may have noticed—although their actions were ensconced in the matheematical resolution of our P.V.-1's, or L.C.-10's, flight performances—two friendly forces of Nature have been accompanying us on our trial runs and have contributed to our velocity build-ups. The first of these velocity-adders is the Earth's 1% lower gravitational pull that exists at the 100-mile level. Gravity's loss turns out to be our P.V.'s gain, because the 1% difference allows us to divert .322 GeeForce (1% of gravity) out of our lift vector and to apply it to the horizontal thrust vector. Of course, at the 100-mile level, the P.V.-1's gain from gravity's diminution is quite small—less than 200 MPH—in com-

parison to the top speed of 17,000 MPH on the record 36-minute
trip. But technically, even in our case, it is worth mentioning.
Earth's gravity effect on proximate objects decreases in proportion to the square of the object distance from the Earth center.
Thus, at 4,000 miles altitude (double our P.V.'s 100-mile "altitude" from Earth center), the acceleration due to gravity is only
8 feet/sec^2, one-fourth of its sea-level value. At 10,000 miles, it
is only 2½ feet/sec^2, a mere 8% of its base effect. Full-time
P.M.I. propelled aerospace vessels become tremendous velocity
accumulators when they do not have to expend their GeeForce
to oppose the powerful—and equally full-time—restraining force
of Earth's gravity. And already, at the 100-mile altitude level,
we were at the threshold, the first 1%, of this important velocity-
additive factor that makes a speed giant out of our constant-
acceleration P.M.I. machine.

The second friendly traveling companion on our cross-country
hops was a generous fellow known as Orbital Aid. He abides by
the strict but simple regimen of $a = v^2/r$ and there is no arguing
with his product. You must take it; you can't leave it or lose it
or ship it back. Centrifugal acceleration, which is what mathematicians and astronomers call our friendly companion, operates in
a direction exactly opposite to Earth's gravitational acceleration.
The value "a" of this outward-directed acceleration—from the
simple formula—is equal to the squared multiple of our vessel's
tangential or "curved" horizontal velocity, divided by the radius
distance of its altitude circle measured from the Earth center.
Most space enthusiasts are familiar with the Orbital Aid formula
in the classic case where an aerospace vessel attains a self-sustaining, weightless, circular orbit at 18,000 MPH on the end of
a 4,200-mile radius that places it about 200 miles in altitude.
But of course, there are an infinite number of solutions besides
the circular orbit to $a = g = v^2/r$.

The weightlessness condition in space is the state of naturally
balanced forces, the state of equilibrium that Nature forever
seeks. All satellites that meet the minimum velocity and directional
requirements for orbit are in a weightless state relative to the
force of universal gravity. An orbiting body's centrifugal acceleration "a," due to its curved revolution about its "Sun" (focus

point), must always equal the acceleration of (universal) gravity "g" that exists at the satellite's instantaneous position in space. And so, as Johannes Kepler the great 16th-century astronomer showed us, orbiting planets and all other satellites, in their natural, mathematical compulsion to balance the forces acting upon them, align themselves into elliptical orbits. On these "eccentric circles" or elliptical paths, satellites are free—mathematically and Nature-ly—to continuously change their velocities and effective radii, in order to produce just enough centrifugal acceleration *"a"* to balance the varying amounts of universal gravity *"g"* that they encounter along their relentless courses.

Our P.V.-1 trial runs between New York and Los Angeles did not have to cope with the complexities of elliptical orbits. But we did get close to orbital speed with our 17,000 MPH peak velocity. The average value of Orbital Aid or centrifugal acceleration developed on our flights amounted to a neat 25 percent of "g," the acceleration due to gravity. This assistance in supporting the P.V.'s 1-ton mass allowed us to divert a corresponding portion of our applied GeeForce into horizontal propulsion vector. Approximately 2,000 MPH of our peak velocity of 17,000 MPH came from this extra kick contributed by good old Orbital Aid.

On a longer journey, where we could easily build up a velocity greater than the orbital *"v"* needed for our fixed 100-mile altitude, we can see that Orbital Aid may become too good a thing, more than we can use. On such a trip, as the *"a"* of centrifugal acceleration increases to exceed the *"g"* of Earth gravity, our P.V.-1 will have to divert more and more of its applied GeeForce to the downward, gravity direction in order to preserve flight plan altitude. When "v" hits 28,000 MPH, the P.V. has reached the limit of its performance at the 100-mile level. At this horizontal velocity, full nominal 1.50 GeeForce must be vectored downward in coincidence with gravity, to oppose the outward, centrifugal v^2/r imposed by the circular, curving motion of our flight path.

Personal Vehicular operation is not without its hazards. The greatest of these is the hidden danger of orbital spin-out. P.V. operators constantly must guard against the comfort and complacency afforded by the quiet of P.M.I.-propelled flight. The least pilot hesitancy or lack of anticipation in navigation, or a "falling asleep at the throttles" attitude, can send a vessel into spatial oblivion. Nature will have mathematical satisfaction in the relationship of universal gravitation, orbital velocity, and orbital radii. There is always the real possibility—when a vessel's E.E.P. (Emergency Effort Propulsion) capability is exceeded—of meeting this satisfaction via permanent spin-out into a "differential" elliptical path—the dreaded hyperbolic orbit that has no return from the vast eternity of space.

BOOM B.A.G.'s—SONIC BOOM ATTENUATION GEAR

Both the L.C.-10 and the P.V.-1, with their respective 750 MPH and 1,000 MPH low altitude velocities, quickly reach sonic speed—Mach 1—on their flight paths through the atmosphere. But the disturbing sonic booms that normally would accompany and follow their trans-sonic passages are now of small consequence. All L.C.-10's and P.V.-1's are standard-equipped with "Concorde Boom BAG's." These Sonic Boom Attenuation Gear were developed and perfected in 1980, in conjunction with the Concorde super-sonic jet-transport program. On-board Boom BAG's are able to capture 99% of the energy of a sonic boom and to deflect it away from the terrestrial carpet. Essentially, Concorde Boom BAG's are three channel audio-attenuation equipment. In avionic circles the equipment is known as T.F.&P. hardware. T.F.&P. hardware Traps, Focuses, and Projects the sonic energy developed at and above Mach I flight. The trapped audio energy is focused (modulated) onto Rayform #14 radio frequency carriers, which are then projected vertically upward into space via radiators with front to back ratios of 100:1. As a consequence of this unique avionics technique, only 1% of the disquieting boom, as a rule, finds its way down to Earth, with negligible physical effect.

EM RAYPATH GUIDANCE
TRAFFIC CONTROLLER OF THE FUTURE

Aside from the great wonder of P.M.I. Propulsion itself, there are literally dozens of marvelous technical innovations built into the four categories of our new aerospace vessels. Sonic Boom Attenuation Gear, the Mark 10^6 Inertial Plane Navigator, and the G-Orienting Bodyseat are just a few of the special equipments that will ensure the success and progressive acceptance of P.M.I. Technology. However, there is urgent need for still another auxiliary technological system. This required system—bearing the Project name, EM Raypath Guidance—has been under vigorous research and development since 1987. By utilizing the latest EM Rayform communciation and data storage techniques, engineers of the EM Raypath Guidance Project hope to perfect a fully automatic system of aerospace traffic control, combined and coordinated with vessel guidance and navigation. The day is not far off—perhaps in less than a generation—when 10's of millions of P.V.'s and other hundreds of thousands of Light Commercials, Medium Commercials, and the ponderous Heavy Transports will fill the skyways around the Earth. And within the coming century, in the vicinity of our extra-planetary colonies, on our Moon and on the friendly satellites of Jupiter and Saturn, P.M.I.-propelled commerce may well encounter similiar rush-hour congestions. To serve this rapidly approaching aerospace complex, and especially to keep the swarms of L.C. and P.V. "bees" from bumping one another, EM Raypath Guidance becomes an absolute requirement.

The Project managers of Raypath Guidance have recently described some of the remarkable progress they have made on their road to the perfection of a working system. In an oversimplification of their ambitious task, they tell us that the Project consists of the collection of myriads of 3-dimensional position data from in-flight vessels, and of communicating these navigational "fixes" into a ground-station network of Traffic Control and Guidance Computers. Under the provisions of the ultimate System, each and every aerospace vessel will run a continuous navigational fix-trace of itself by means of an on-board 10-line LORAX (Locus of Raypath Airspace Fixes) calculator. The LORAX will constantly receive lines-and-lengths of position from 10 terrestrial transmitting stations convenient to the vessel's course. The LORAX product, the continuous 3-dimensional fix-trace of the vessel in the airspace, is to be relay-transmitted into T.C.&G. (Traffic

Control and Guidance) centers. At these ground stations, T.C.& G. computers will analyze the data to determine: forward fix predictions, competitive course intersections, airspace saturation, skypath availability, and flight plan assignments. Additionally, Raypath T.C. & G. stations will monitor and feed back to each vessel an accurate GeeForce throttle setting and P.M.I. (Projected Image) position, to guide the flight on a safe sub-orbital or full-orbital course to its destination.

Coincidentally and fortunately, the Raypath Guidance problem shares many of the physical dimensions of EM Weather Control Technology. The basic 10 × 10 × 10 mile Local Weather Control operating block turns out to be an ideally sized unit airspace block for the Raypath Guidance System. By taking advantage of this "workspace" similarity, Raypath Guidance will be able to acquire the necessary geographic coverage and accuracy needed in its own network. Present planning calls for both of these emerging EM Technologies to standardize on the 1,000 cubic-mile Local block, and for the co-location of Raypath Guidance System computers and Weather Control apparatus at the same control-site corners. The 1,000 cubic-mile unit block of airspace—in EM Raypath Guidance—will be sub-divided into three operational classifications, related volumetrically to the unit block in ratios of: Milli (1/1,000), Micro (1/1,000,000), and Nano (1/1,000,000,000). Thus, the 1 cubic-mile Milliblock has sides of 1 mile, the Microblock (1/1,000 cubic mile) sides of .1 mile or 600 feet, and the Nanoblock (1/1,000,000 cubic mile) sides of .01 or 60 feet.

Raypath flight clearances, during conditions of low traffic volume and cross-country travel, normally would be issued on Milliblock standards; that is, with no closer than 1 mile proximity between any two randomly coursed vessels. Under Milliblock clearances, some 1,000 aerospace vessels could operate concurrently in the 10 × 10 × 10 mile (1,000 cubic mile) unit airspace. And with stacking to the 100 mile level, 10,000 vessels may be accommodated at this ultra safe 1 mile separation. To provide an overlapping surveillance of the airspace within adjacent 1 cubic-mile Milliblocks—so that perimeters of airspace blocks receive the same relative inspection as centers—the scan and search technique at all Raypath Guidance centers will utilize "centerline-shift" on alternate scans. For Milliblock airspace security, the alternating side-shift will be one-half mile.

The next lesser degree of operational safety, Microblock clearance, has a gross occupancy potential of 1 million P.M.I. vessels per 1,000 cubic-mile unit airspace block. Stacking to the 100-mile level can multiply this tremendous capacity ten times more. Obviously, such P.M.I. vessel concentrations are very improbable. The Raypath System's designers, therefore, have elected to capitalize on this opportunity for added safety, by reducing Microblock occupancy to an extreme 30% of its volumetric potential. This conservative approach guarantees—at a safety factor of more than 3 times—an absolute 600-foot minimum separation between the 300,000 aerospace vessels that may at one time occupy a unit block. In the present stage of Raypath Traffic Control and Guidance, it appears that the 30% modified Microblock airtraffic clearance will provide a practicable and completely safe airspace saturation over the busiest cities, even during pre-holiday rush hours. Constant protection against collision-course programming will be insured by T.C. & G. computer examination of traffic at the Nanoblock 60-foot separation standard, and with flight clearances issued at the Microblock 600-foot standard—an additional safety margin of 10 times.

Standard cross-country flights and low traffic volume operations —governed by Milliblock 1-mile separations—will also be computer examined at the Nanoblock 60-foot separation, establishing a safety margin of 100 times. Although the Raypath System T.C. & G. computers will be under no functional stress to run this double resolution—from Nano thru Micro to Milli—Milliblock clearances approach the case of "How safe can you be?"

In essence then, under the eventual and ultimate System of EM Raypath Guidance, all routings between points on the Earth become computerized traces trajecting through countless 60-foot Nanoblocks of airspace. In a worldwide network of Raypath Traffic Control and Guidance stations, these traces are advanced to predict the occupancy status in each airspace block during forward periods of time, applicable to the simultaneous flight plans of millions of P.M.I. aerospace vessels. Traffic clearances and vessel guidance orders are then—and continuously—issued, corresponding to the network's course-interference search and analysis.

Incidentally, all airspace blocks, from the 10^3 cubic-mile unit block down to the 10^{-6} cubic-mile Nanoblock, can be scanned for vessel occupancy in as fine a time period as 1 nano-second (1/1,000,000,000 second). But 10^{-9} nano, and even 10^{-6} micro, scan-timing schedules will find little practical use in Raypath Guidance until P.M.I. vessels begin to operate in the velocity ranges approaching Lach 1, the 186,000-mile-per-second speed of light. The more reasonable, and perceptible, milli-second (1/1,000 second) of time will be the popular scanning increment of present-day Raypath Technology. Milli-second scanning will render adequate airspace occupancy checks on all of the "slow-moving" vessels of our era as they operate in the restricted velocity environment of the Earth's atmosphere. Even at vessel speeds of 30,000 MPH, beyond the atmospheric level, milli-second scan-timing will still be compatible with Nanoblock surveillance, registering a fix-trace 50 feet in length on each scan.

Although we are still a long way from the need for the nano-second level of definition and perfection being designed into the EM Raypath Guidance System, it is reassuring to recognize that Rayform communication techniques make such accuracies possible. With this kind of technological reserve supporting the Project, we can look forward to a finalization and delivery of the System, surely within the decade, as promised by its dedicated managers. Until that time, we must creep along with on-board pilot control, and a strict adherence to the FSFR and MSFR traffic regulations applicable to each of the four vessel-categories. Yet—our enthusiasm and confidence for the eventual completion of the System compel us to speculate a step further into the forthcoming wonder of everyday P.M.I. travel aided by EM Raypath Guidance—as it will apply to the average Personal Vehicular operator.

SO, LET'S TAKE ANOTHER TRIP
THIS TIME, RAYPATH GUIDED

Once upon a day not too far in our merging futurity, a P.V.-1's proud owner—perhaps you or I—will finish his breakfast, bid the family the usual farewell and wishes for a good day, and walk to the garage-port attached to the rear of his home. As he climbs aboard his 1-ton double-lens-shaped sedan and secures himself into the left front bodyseat, the garage roof, almost seeming to sense the oncoming adventure, quietly slides open to the boundless sky. If it is a typical working day, our Personal Vehicular owner-pilot will file a flight-plan request for a routine commutation to the office or plant. Or, if happily, it is the week end—and the entire family complete with picnic baskets is on board with him—our family hero may just as easily file for flight clearance to either of their vacation-cottage retreats, the one in central Australia or the other in the African Sahara. His filing action to the Local Raypath Guidance station is no more complicated than dialing a 10-digit telephone number. Dialed input options include destination code and preferences of altitude, departure angle, type of flight plan (Full-Square or Modified-Square), and percent of P.M.I. GeeForce nominal. As an alternate filing procedure preferred by more than 90% of today's confident Personal Vehicular operators, our pilot may simply leave all details to the Raypath Guidance computer by dialing destination code plus 999, indicating "Best Way—Raypath Computer Option." Computer-Option clearances will always result in the shortest trip-times, based on nominal power settings and flight plan rules; and the variety of routing solutions that the "free-hand" Raypath computer grinds out are sometimes interesting, and certainly always, refreshing for the frequent traveler.

Despite the possibility that thousands of other P.V. pilots are dialing for flight clearances, Local Raypath Guidance will return confirmation to our owner-operator within seconds, by Green-Lighting the master Lift-Off switch on the vessel's Raypath auto-control console. Once Green-Light is accepted by the pilot's master switch initiation action, the P.V.-1, in complete magnetic silence and with scarcely a rustle to the nearby trees and shrubbery, lifts off ever so smoothly through the garage-roof aperture. Now clear of neighborhood rooftops, the P.V.-1 immediately locks onto the course and flight program calculated by Raypath Guidance and relayed into the on-board Raypath auto-control. A running plot of the navigation—a fix-trace of the P.V.'s route through the airspace—shows up on the display face of the LORAX, while continuous up-dates on the applied GeeForce and Image-projection angle register on the auto-control panel. And if, as it sometimes happens in all human planning, the pilot decides to change his options during the flight, there is no reason for him to defer his wishes or revised judgment. The network Raypath Guidance stations that are monitoring the flight will readily accept a new set of in-flight options. After a second or two to calculate the navigational solution and to inspect the airspace for competitive course intersections, the System's controlling ground station will Green-Light Local, Zonal, and Regional —and in fact, worldwide—readiness, and will await initiation action from the vessel's operator. Aboard the P.V.-1, the smooth turn-around or course adjustment becomes just another routine maneuver.

(The ease with which in-flight program changes are handled is illustrated by the "continuous change" packaged flight plans that Raypath Guidance offers to the Personal Vehicular public. Some 100 different 1-, 2-, and 3-hour sight-seeing and familiarization tours, following complex quadratic patterns through the sky, are listed by the System's Promotional Division and are available by merely dialing simplified input-option numbers. Many thousands of P.V families take advantage of this pre-programmed Raypath service, particularly on a relaxing Sunday afternoon, by cutting 3-dimensional figure "8's" and drawing beautiful 4-leaf "Roses" whose petals reach from the Atlantic to the Pacific.)

Finally, on landing, even though our dauntless Personal Vehicular is now halfway round the world, the on-board Raypath auto-control panel acknowledges flight plan closure to the network, and all boards are cleared. During the entire flight, across the sparsely populated prairie skies and through the saturated metropolitan airspaces, our Raypath-Guided P.V. has followed a sky-path reserved for it alone. And not unlike one of a million honey bees circling the hive, our P.V. "bee" occasionally may glimpse a fellow traveler zipping by. But both Nature's gifted navigator and the P.V.-1 fly their missions with a common trust that their Guidance Systems are ever alert to guarantee the integrity of their flight plans and to protect them—each and every single one —from a multiple occupancy of their reserved and confirmed airspaces.

*   *   *

SPEAKING ABOUT THE FUTURE

Can you picture young Johnny and Joey, two exuberant grade-schoolers, on their way to Monday morning classes. Johnny is especially wound up today, a holdover from the excitement of yesterday's excursion to the Moon in the family P.V. It was Johnny's first trip to the colonies and he is bubbling over to tell his pal, Joey, all about the Moon, and how he had been assistant navigator to his dad on their 4-hour runs, going and coming.

Beaming with the pride of Sunday's achievement, Johnny opens the conversation with: "Say Joey, what do you think we did yesterday? We saw Copernicus and had lunch with the colonists at Fra Mauro!"

To which Joey—who has already been there a dozen times, and in the nonchalance and acceptance of children born into the wonders of our Age; and knowing nothing less—indifferently replies, "Big deal, Johnny. So what else is new?"

Flysheet Comments

During the writing of *The EM Discoveries*—as, I suppose, in the gathering of any narrative—several personal "asides" came into mind. They would not go away until I gave them a line or two. The collection of these side thoughts into a rather heavy lining that I call Flysheet Comments is offered herewith as a preview—perhaps even as a warning—to the EM Age adventurer. But also, and hopefully, these comments may dispose the daring futuristic traveler toward a reading attitude that will provide present meaning and reality to the fabulous *EM Discoveries*.

REG

1. There probably is a conclusion in *The EM Discoveries* different and suited to each individual reader.

2. A "low-key" science fiction story dealing with basic reasonable technologies, and with the physical principles of their foundations. A plain-language technical analysis of three particular, but commonplace technologies that make their appearance in A.D. 1985.

3. I hope that *The EM Discoveries* is a different kind of book, one that is enjoyable, amusing, and mildly provocative.

4. While it is in the category of science "factually backed" fiction and told with current world political problems as a background, it is not fault-finding and tries to be a forward-looking effort.

5. Somewhere along the pages, depending on where you chose to draw the line between reality and imagination, you will get

168

the idea—the message, the word—that one must roll up his pantlegs a few turns, as the subject gets farther "out."

6. I have read many parenthetically organized textbooks, I thought it would be nice to get even, by winding up a few whoppers—in the same pattern.

7. The Prologue is almost a sin in its serious disguise. And the story of Weather Control tends to be serious in the beginning, but it lightens up a bit toward the end.

8. "What are you—some kind of technological evangelist!"

9. Written by the ultimate (should I say the lowest) grade of S-F writer: a genuine S-F con artist.

10. Pure unadulterated **BS**.

11. There is a cycle within the stories—a cycle of "serious" blending off into "tongue-in-cheek." A mixing of the serious approach to scientific and political ideas with a deep tongue-in-cheek attitude associated with the telling of "whoppers."

12. If the world has to wait for such a solution to its political and social dilemmas, God help us. This is the serious theme.

13. Chalk one up for Science. Why says it is not as strong as Love, and that it will not be a powerful co-agent in saving, humanizing, and preserving our world.

14. We have been taking our ecological problems, at least some of them, too seriously. The world isn't all that bad off. It's about time we look at a few brighter sides of Nature and allow God an opportunity to help us straighten out the presently worrisome ones.

15. What kind of a nut could put together something like this?

16.   This guy can't be serious. But why did it take me so many pages to find that out?

17.   Enjoy *The EM Discoveries* simply for its whopper type science stories. Don't believe in the Discoveries—yet. They are still a fantasy in our time. But in another 10 years, hold onto your hat, because here we go!

18.   An enigmatic mixture of the serious, fantastic, and ludicrous; not necessarily in that order of predominance or merit.

19.   Technically credible, mathematically accurate. Why not? Plausible. Who can say. Wouldn't it be great—if!

20.   I don't subscribe to the popular advertising philosophy that we are a world of busy, intellectual people who could care less about the technological aspects of our culture. We *are* interested in "what's under the hood."

21.   The narrative expresses a concern for the future, and an implied admission that present scientific and technological exploitation denies a responsibility for this continuing future that belongs to the next generation, and the next, and the next.

22.   What an injustice to all the sincere people of our great land who will believe this "serious" story of our troubled times. They may never be the same.

23.   Low-key science fantasy. A course in GeeForce, with a bit of algebra, mechanics, chemistry, meteorology, astronomy, geology, electricity, and even some agronomy—all mixed in and "up."

24.   Sometimes it is embarrassing to lie like this, even in a "literary" spoof.

25.   You will utterly confuse every schoolboy who is attempting

to learn his physics and chemistry. Some of them may prefer to believe your version (or inversion) of science. But those who see through your wild fabrications will survive, and perhaps be better for it.

26. Do you suppose some students might even believe your weirdo explanations of science—or wish to—over the equally fantastic hypotheses printed in their textbooks?

27. The dream, the fantasy, of Weather Control rambles on to 30,000 words. After some 20 pages I hope you will begin to smile and enjoy the story—if there is one—and keep the technical slant to the background. And next, in Elemental Separation, of course, you will find the ideal solution to the problem of pollution! And finally, if you plan to travel, be sure that your airliner is P.M.I. equipped. There's no better way to fly.

28. Hopefully, the fantasies of the 100 EM Rayforms—and of their particular technological capabilities—are within the grasp of today's space-oriented, electronically sophisticated average housewife, schoolboy, schoolgirl, hot-rod enthusiast—the apparatus operators of our times.

29. Today's reader, today's citizen cannot forever live (and hide) in provincial castles of peace and love, sports and politics, daily work routine—within the narrow limits of professionalism and specialty occupation. He must recognize the roles of all the elements in our culture: Science, Nationalism, Humanitarianism, Religion. Will we ever achieve a harmony of these human motivations—on national levels, and on personal levels as well? Does the human race really want to; or is this idea—a search for a harmony of the human motivations—a goal that appeals and qualifies itself only to some? And if the world's destiny rests upon these few, which faction among them will be right in its choice of human purpose and destination? And when the opportunity is at hand, which faction will prosper in the pursuit of this goal; or survive, if it comes to that?

30.   As I finish reading each of the topical paragraphs and start on the next, I find myself almost laughing out loud—at least chuckling to myself—and thinking, "After that whopper, does this guy have still another. Doesn't he embarrass?" But somehow, they do seem to roll together into a provocative, though especially I hope, an amusing story. Serious Science, however, is sure taking a beating. And so is "super-seriousness" itself.

31.   Gosh, it sometimes sounds like something from Buckminster Fuller, the whole earth man. Well, maybe that isn't bad company. I would hope he thinks so too—and glad we agree on some points. But honestly, I never heard of him until reading Jeanne's birthday gift, the *Whole Earth Catalog,* received on June 30, 1972; and a Cleveland P.D. article by George Barmann on July 4, 1972. All of which proves I don't do a good job of outside reading. In fact, I hear a fellow named Orwell wrote a swell story called *1984.* Sure would like to read it. Isn't it a shame to lock yourself (myself) out of some pleasures because you are afraid you might lose your "exclusivity"? At any rate, Fuller's or Jeanne's or Orwell's or anyone's ideas are not exclusive, and we all align our thoughts cause-and-effect-wise, or problem-and-solution-wise along similar routes, selectively guided by our personal experience and background. So isn't this the way in most matters?

32.   If *The EM Discoveries* is reminiscent of #31 (*The Whole Earth Catalog,* and so on), the difference in *The EM Discoveries* lies in its solution to present world problems via the fantasy of the 100 EM Rayforms. Whereas, I suppose, the whole-earth cult expects in and by its realism to accomplish a solution using what is already at hand, or do they? Or is there enough there to give them a chance for success? Or is it inevitable that we must continue forever along the present road confined to the natural and the technological environments of today?

33.   This is a specific, non-general, technical, engineering-oriented approach to the A.D. 2000 story, as opposed to the sociological or psychological (non-technical) slant. It is not at all like the

Future Shock story (read July 14, 1972), which is a non-technical generalization slanted to the great number of perplexed city folks who find in it *(Future Shock)* a name for their personal inadequacies in modern times. The future is not made for those who will have problems adapting to it, but perhaps this is the group in society that buys most of the books. (That's sort of cruel, Bob. Where are your manners?)

In the final analysis, the world is hard and cold. You must qualify individually and personally for your place. You must adapt and re-adapt. You must work at it, you must work, you must merit your pay or lose. Nature—and the world is just one of Her smallest stages—is a dispassionate taskmaster. The continuing process of adapting to Nature may even be called Evolution of the Species.

34.   If we limit our imaginations of the future in the fields of Technology, Sociology, Ecology, Economics—we are purposefully closing our minds on ourselves. A passive disinterest in these subjects is hardly possible; a disinterest per se is intentional, as is a diversion of our interests to other limited, restricted, worthless subjects, or selfish preferences. And the failure to seek information and self-education on a broad plain is equally a serious travesty against ourselves.

35.   I hope you will find a few chuckles—of amusement, skepticism, and perhaps even agreement—in reading these chapters.

36.   We are all futurologists and we should be. It is our present duty and responsibility. Man's place in our planet's ecology as a controller of the course and pace of life and of the future of the species compels us to be futurologists.

37.   A preponderance of pessimism lately surrounds us, both literary and vocal, championed by the faultfinders who have weaseled their way into becoming the most-listened-to of our crop of self-appointed spokesmen. Why is it that so many of today's most articulate future-observer analysts peddle pessimism and

even debauch themselves in suicidal recriminations? But most
aspects—if not all of them—of the future are far from negative,
and it is just as likely that the Unknown Future holds great
treasures for us, as it is that we are a race and planet doomed.

38.   *The EM Discoveries*—Subject Classification: Optimistic
Futurology. A technical accounting, in plain language, of the
Next Major Scientific Breakthrough and of three very probable
new technologies that may revolutionize (and save) our human
culture.

39.   Man's uptrend—his reach along the road toward his true
purpose in the Universe—is a far greater possibility than his or
the planet's demise.
Analogy: Planets and celestial bodies in collision—a fear more
than a proven physical, natural reality. In the billions of galaxies
(there are some 3,000 billion), each holding billions of stars like
our Sun (our Milky Way Galaxy has 100 billion stars and "nearby" Andromeda holds several thousand billion stars) there is
little sign of collision between the bodies within a system. Stellar
(and Galactic) evolution appears to take other courses: gaseous
adsorption, condensation, and explosive sublimation, and do not
concern themselves with their own demise resulting from collisions
and the fear of collisions. (I think there is some kind of analogy
hidden in there somewhere.)

40.   Astronomy. It's got to be the most fascinating subject in
the world and the one subject most closely linked to future
science. Hold on—if you are still aboard—for the sequel to
this primordial effort, *The EM Discoveries*. It is now in the mill
and if I ever get on the ball, with the help of a few rainy days
to keep me indoors, it may be called: *From William Josephs'
Notebook*. But I don't believe Albert Einstein and his friends
would accept all of the *Notebook's* propositions. Albert, who of
course will always be most respected, and who as fine a scholar
and gentleman as ever we were blessed to share, was really a
bit "provincial." And I may be more than a bit brazen in making

so crude a suggestion. But I am neither the originator nor an authority of this impeachment, though merely and surely an interested observer.

Einstein's Theory of Relativity tells us via $E = mc^2$ that energy is mass multipled by a factor of velocity. And this brief but profound formula tells us, in extension, that the mass of an electron—and who knows what else—actually *increases* with its structural velocity. Expressed in an alternate way, these last two sentences say there can never be a velocity greater than *"c,"* the speed of light (186,000 miles per second), because any increase in *"c"* turns itself off automatically by the transition of the increased mass into energy.

But now, hear this: According to modern authorities in the Physical and Astronomical Sciences, Albert Einstein's brilliant but confining Law, the Theory of Relativity, is postulated only on the experience and observation of matter within the *Observable* Universe. Sir Isaac Newton's Law of Universal Gravity is defined in this same arena. Today, our foremost observers in this infant Science of Astronomy believe that at least 80 percent of the *Total* Universe lies ouside of the *Observable* Universe. This recent hypothesis—that *beyond* the Quasars and Black Holes that abound in the extremes of the Observable Universe at Hubble's R (R, the radius distance from the Earth to the end of the Observable Universe equals 10^{10} light years) there lies 80 percent of the Total Universe—makes Einstein and Newton and our other pioneer physical scientists absolutely correct within the sphere of the Observable Universe, but perhaps only 20 percent correct in the meaning and accuracy of their Physical Laws relative to the total entity of God's Heavens. It is with the highest respect, yet with an open mind, that soon we may find Albert and Sir Isaac to have been—"provincial."

41. *The EM Discoveries* deals with Science in the Future. You will hardly stop—I hope—to realize or to call the story science fiction; although, in the areas where this classification fits, *The EM Discoveries* is proud to be so categorized.

Robert Gibbons, A.D. 1973

(—and with permission, A.D. 2973)